Food Irradiation: A Sourcebook

FOOD
IRRADIATION

A SOURCEBOOK

Edited by **E. A. MURANO**

Written by **D. J. HAYES**
E. A. MURANO
P. S. MURANO
D. G. OLSON
S. G. SAPP

IOWA STATE UNIVERSITY PRESS / AMES

E. A. MURANO received her PhD in food science and technology from Virginia Polytechnic Institute and State University, Blacksburg. She is professor-in-charge of research programs at the linear accelerator facility, Iowa State University, Ames.

D. J. HAYES received his PhD in international trade from the University of California, Berkeley. He is leader of the Trade and Agricultural Policy Division, Center for Agricultural and Rural Development, Iowa State University, Ames.

P. S. MURANO received his PhD in human nutrition and foods from Virginia Polytechnic Institute and State University, Blacksburg. He is affiliate assistant professor, Department of Food Science and Human Nutrition, and Department of Microbiology, Immunology and Preventive Medicine, Iowa State University, Ames.

D. G. OLSON received his PhD in meat science from Iowa State University, Ames. He is director of the Utilization Center for Agricultural Products, Iowa Agricultural Experiment Station, Iowa State University, Ames.

S. G. SAPP received his PhD in sociology from Texas A&M University, College Station. He is associate professor in the Department of Sociology, Iowa State University, Ames. His research emphasis is on consumer preferences for red meats in foreign and domestic markets, consumer acceptance of agricultural technology, and social determinates of human food consumption and nutrition.

♾ Printed on acid-free paper in the United States of America

First edition, 1995

Library of Congress Cataloging-in-Publication Data

Food irradiation: a sourcebook/edited by E. A. Murano: written by D. J. Hayes ... [et al.].—1st ed.
    p.   cm.
  Includes bibliographical references and index.
  ISBN 0-8138-2060-X
  1. Radiation processing of food. I. Murano, E. A.   II. Hayes, D. J.
TP371.8.F638   1995
668'.0288—dc20   95-10982

CONTENTS

FOREWORD

The United States and perhaps the world is in the midst of a food safety revolution. Events over the past 2 to 3 years have focused the world's attention on food safety. It has become obvious that current organoleptic (sight, feel, and smell) inspection systems are not adequate to protect against bacteria that cause foodborne illness. It has also become obvious that the current systems of food production contain inadequate bacterial interventions (kill or reduction steps). Today, the only bacterial interventions for meat and poultry are antibacterial rinses during the slaughter process, and the final cooking stage. Food safety systems of the future will hopefully contain sequential bacterial interventions that, collectively, will substantially reduce risk. Food irradiation is perhaps the most effective intervention available today.

The editor and authors of *Food Irradiation: A Sourcebook* have done an outstanding job of putting the entire food irradiation subject into proper perspective. Dr. Olson (Chapter 1) gives a clear description of the food irradiation process, including an excellent comparison of gamma versus electron beam irradiation. Dr. E. Murano (Chapter 2) provides a clear and concise overview of food microbiology and the effects of irradiation. Of particular interest is the section dealing with factors effecting the destruction of microorganisms. Dr. E. Murano's chapter does an excellent job of covering all food (meat, poultry, fruits, vegetables, etc.). Chapter 3 (Dr. P. Murano) addresses all aspects of food irradiation and quality (nutrition, taste, etc.). Dr. Sapp (Chapter 4 on consumer acceptance) does an excellent job of identifying the current state of the knowledge regarding consumer acceptance and attitudes. Chapter 4 also concentrates on communication and perception issues that need further attention. Dr. Hayes (Chapter 5) clearly discusses the economic issues surrounding irradiation. Dr. Hayes goes into significant detail regarding costs and benefits.

In summary, the authors of *Food Irradiation* have put together an excellent text that will serve as a good resource text. They are to be congratulated.

H. RUSSELL CROSS
Institute of Food Science and Engineering
Texas A&M University

PREFACE

Without practical thinking, pasteurisation
would just be what Mme. Pasteur
endured during her husband's
loud snoring.

ALEXANDER FLEMING
on receiving Nobel Prize
for discovering penicillin

In recent years we, the consumers, have been bombarded with a myriad of reports regarding the apparent lack of safety of our food supply. With hidden cameras, the major television networks have surprised us, even shocked us, with their accounts of microbial contamination of fresh meats and vegetables. Along the way, solutions to this problem are rarely offered, beyond such approaches as demanding that the United States Department of Agriculture (USDA) hire more meat inspectors and that no product be allowed to be sold if it is contaminated with microorganisms. The former will only help if these inspectors are able to detect bacterial contamination the moment carcasses pass them on their way to the cooler, and the latter is virtually impossible, given the ubiquitousness of the microbial world.

The science of foods has been very successful at devising solutions to the problem of microbial contamination, and as a result, has provided ways in which foods can be made safe from pathogens such as *Salmonella*, *Listeria*, and the now famous *Escherichia coli* serotype O157:H7. Among these are: refrigeration, freezing, heating, modified atmosphere packaging, and chemical preservatives (both natural and manufactured). Like all processing methods, they have their specific uses, and none is able to solve all the problems of contamination by itself. In addition, sanitary practices on the farm, as well as postharvest, play a significant role on the microbial quality of the product before it even gets to the processing stage.

Food irradiation is a technology that holds much promise in increasing the safety of our food supply, because it offers several advantages to the above methods. First, product quality is not affected any more than it is by other treatments, with irradiated products often being ranked as more desirable than nonirradiated foods. Second, the product is irradiated after being packaged, a definite advantage in eliminating cross-contamination. Third, irradiation offers a critical control point to the consumer: failure to achieve a particular internal temperature during cooking of a product (from which bacterial contaminants have been eliminated by irradiation) will not spell morbidity, or mortality, to the person consuming that food.

The story of food irradiation dates back to the 1950s, and even earlier, when scientists looked for ways in which the power of the atom could be used for peaceful purposes. Since then, over 30 countries have approved the use of this technology for disinfestation and disinfection of fresh foods, with the United States actually lagging behind in the use of irradiation to increase food safety. An expert committee, comprised of scientists from all over the world, reviewed all the studies conducted up to the 1970s on the safety and wholesomeness of irradiated foods. In 1980, the committee, which included members of the Food and Agriculture Organization of the United Nations, the World Health Organization, and the International Atomic Energy Agency, declared irradiated foods to be safe, and in fact, endorsed the use of this technology worldwide.

Since then, there have been various events taking place in the United States that have prompted consumers, food companies, regulators, and the media to look at the use of food irradiation for improving the safety of our food supply. One such event was an outbreak of foodborne illness caused by the organism *E. coli* O157:H7 in the Pacific Northwest early in 1993. As a result of this outbreak, at least 2 children died from consumption of undercooked ground beef patties contaminated with this organism. Additional cases have occurred throughout the country, prompting the USDA to declare this microorganism an "adulterant" of fresh beef.

As members of the research team at the Linear Accelerator Facility at Iowa State University, we have received many inquiries regarding the technology of food irradiation. Since March of 1993, when the ISU facility became operational, we have conducted dozens of tours and met with many consumer and industry groups, all wanting to learn about the potential uses of this technology to improve food safety. It became obvious to us that, even though food irradiation has been around for decades, and many volumes have been written on the subject, there is no single source where a consumer, a reporter, a regulator, an industry executive, or a policymaker could go to find information on the practical uses of this technology. Many books are too technical for some of these groups, are outdated, or focus on already settled issues, such as the wholesomeness or toxicology of irradiated foods, both of which have been addressed very satisfactorily by over 40 years of research worldwide.

We embarked on the writing of this book because we wanted to provide the information we thought was needed by the groups listed above, and to do so in a way that would be easy to understand by all. The subject of food irradiation encompasses physics, radiation chemistry, nuclear engineering, food science, microbiology, economics, and sociology, to name a few. Thus, our challenge has been to simplify the material wherever possible while keeping faithful to the factual accuracy of the contents. The technical information provided in the various chapters is worded in such a way as to give the book "user-friendliness" without compromising its usefulness. This book is not intended for scientists or irradiation experts, although it certainly can serve to update these groups on the subject. Rather, it is addressed to members of industry, regulatory agencies, legislators, and the media to provide a *practical* source of information on food irradiation. Our intent was to focus on current technology, rather than to try to discuss the entire body of knowledge.

As mentioned above, food irradiation has been approved by the U.S. Food and Drug Administration, as well as by many agencies throughout the world. Thus, in writing this book, we opted not to discuss the topic of wholesomeness of irradiated foods, since this issue has been rendered moot by over 40 years of research worldwide.

The chapters were chosen according to the information we thought would be of the greatest benefit to the readers. Chapter 1 contains the basics of food irradiation, with definitions, a discussion on the benefits of this technology, and the current status of government approval in the United States. In addition, practical information on packaging materials that can be used in irradiating food products, dosimetry, and facility planning are included, which should contribute greatly towards providing the food industry with up-to-date information on these subjects.

Chapters 2 and 3 are designed to provide basic information on the effects of irradiation on safety and quality issues. The chapter on the Microbiology of Irradiated Foods (Chapter 2) was written in a straightforward manner, providing some background on general microbiology for nonscientists, as well as practical information on the types of decimal reductions of microbial contaminants that can be achieved with this technology in various food products. The use of food irradiation as a Critical Control Point as part of a Hazard Analysis Critical Control Point (HACCP) System is also discussed, as well as the use of this technology in combination with other processing methods in a hurdle approach to food safety. The chapter on Quality of Irradiated Foods (Chapter 3) deals with the all-important questions of quality changes due to irradiation. This chapter includes the latest information on this issue, including effects on nutrients in comparison with other processing treatments. Data from experiments carried out at Iowa State University regarding consumer sensory evaluation and preference studies of irradiated fresh meats is also included. Some discussion on methods used in detecting whether foods have been irradiated is provided, along with a discussion on the lack of evidence for the presence of unique radicals in irradiated products.

Chapter 4 is dedicated to the subject of consumer acceptance, providing the reader with some background information on the debate over food irradiation between the scientific community and political activists. The latest information on consumer acceptance studies, such as the selling of irradiated poultry in Chicago and Florida is included, with a section containing a listing of the most commonly cited consumer issues.

Finally, Chapter 5 contains valuable facts on what the public may be willing to pay for irradiated foods, once their benefits are explained, along with a way to determine the cost of using such technology. A section on marketing of irradiated foods is included, as well as a section on the capital and other costs that would be incurred by a company wanting to get started using this process.

We hope that this book will be used by its readers as a "how-to" manual on food irradiation, and that it supplies the needed information in a comprehensive yet comprehensible manner. In writing it, we honor all those scientists and food professionals who have worked and who continue to work so diligently towards applying this technology for enhancing food safety. In addition, we salute the consumers of irradiated products, for they will reap the benefits of their efforts.

INTRODUCTION

It's Time for Food Irradiation

JAMES H. STEELE

R esearch on the irradiation of food began in 1895 by German and French scientists using the newly discovered Roentgen x-rays. Not until the 1960s, with the growth of research on the uses of atomic energy, was the broad application of radiation sterilization and pasteurization put to peaceful use in the preservation of food, sterilization of medical supplies, and the structural changes of building materials.

Congress decreed in 1958 that the irradiation of food was a food additive. In 1968, this technology was available for public health application in food protection and preservation and received positive endorsement from the World Congress on the Peacetime Use of Atomic Energy in Geneva, followed by the World Health Organization (WHO), the Food and Agriculture Organization (FAO) scientists, the International Atomic Energy Agency, and other international agencies, scientists, and some government officials. However, political interpretation was otherwise; without approval from higher authorities, food irradiation stalled.

The Food and Drug Administration (FDA) was responsible for reviewing the process for safety and approving the application of irradiation to food, including meat and poultry. That review was completed in

1980, and in 1984 the Secretary of Health and Human Services, Margaret Heckler, endorsed the use of irradiation for food. Within a few years, guidelines for the use of irradiation for food were in place.

Food irradiation is now recognized as another method of preserving food and ensuring its wholesomeness by sterilization or cold pasteurization, and it has diverse application worldwide. If one were to tabulate the food-borne infections related to poultry and meat due to *Salmonella, Campylobacter, Yersinia, Listeria,* and *Escherichia coli,* the totals would exceed hundreds of thousands if not millions of human illnesses. This morbidity and medical expense of meat- and poultry-borne diseases can be prevented.

In 1992, after another extensive review of all existing data, WHO concluded that

> Irradiated food produced under established Good Manufacturing Practices is … safe…. Irradiation will not introduce changes in the composition of food which, from a toxicological point of view, would impose an adverse effect on human health, … will not introduce changes in the microflora of the food which would increase the microbiological risk to the consumer, … will not introduce nutrient losses which … would impose an adverse effect on the nutritional status of individuals or populations.

In 1993, the American Medical Association's Council on Scientific Affairs affirmed food irradiation as "a safe and effective process that increases the safety of food when applied according to governing regulations."

Those who are opposed to using irradiation of food to destroy pathogens that cause food-borne illness voice the same arguments that were voiced against pasteurization at the beginning of the century, or against canned or frozen food—that it would result in poor nutrition and would be dangerous to public health and safety. To belie this consumer fear or indifference, one can cite the USDA survey of consumer attitude research and actual market tests: Susan Conley, of the USDA Food and Safety Inspection Service, found that 70% of the American public wants safe food and will accept food irradiation to ensure its being so; a University of California survey found Californians of the same mind; a

University of Georgia survey found the consumer willing to pay more for irradiated food that would offer the same protection as pasteurized food; several national consumer surveys report that consumers want an opportunity to test irradiated food. Iowa State University surveys cited in this book indicate consumer acceptance of irradiated food in Iowa.

James Mason, M.D., Assistant Secretary of Health, U.S. Department of Health and Human Services, in 1992 endorsed the importance and value of food irradiation in an editorial in *Public Health Reports.* Philip Lee, M.D., now Assistant Secretary for Health Director, US Public Health Service, in a 1994 editorial in the *Journal of the American Medical Association* (*JAMA* 272[4]:261) states,

> Food irradiation, like pasteurization of milk, can prevent countless infections because it destroys the pathogens that cause foodborne illness. Irradiation would neither replace good manufacturing practices nor provide the sole answer to foodborne illnesses. But it would add substantially to a farm-to-table approach for food safety.

The editor and authors of this book are to be congratulated for bringing together for the media and consumers information needed to facilitate the use of food irradiation to protect the public health.

Food Irradiation: A Sourcebook

C H A P T E R   1

IRRADIATION PROCESSING

DENNIS G. OLSON, PhD

Introduction

Irradiation processing of foods has been approved in over 38 countries. Commercial food irradiation is occurring in 30 pilot plants and commercial plants in 25 countries.[9] It has been estimated[8] that over 80 commercial plants will be irradiating food products by the late 1990s. In the United States there is only one dedicated irradiation plant for food, hence most food irradiation occurs outside the United States. With recent demands for control of pathogenic microorganisms in meat, especially ground beef and poultry, the need for additional plants in the United States may develop rapidly. The following is an overview of food irradiation. Further information can be found in Report No. 109, published by the Council for Agricultural Science and Technology, Ames, Iowa.[4]

OVERVIEW OF FOOD IRRADIATION

For centuries, humanity has searched for ways in which food can be preserved, with the ultimate goal of making foods last longer and be safer for human consumption. Methods such as curing and storage of foods at low temperatures are among the oldest food preservation techniques known. Canning, pasteurization, and deep freezing, all developed for commercial application in this century, have been used with a

3

relatively high degree of success. The most recent addition to food preservation technologies is the use of ionizing radiation. This technique has distinct advantages over conventional methods, one being that foods can be treated after packaging, eliminating contamination of foods after processing. In addition, food irradiation preserves foods with minimal loss of quality while leaving no residues.

The food irradiation program began in the United States as a result of the "Atoms for Peace" program established by President Eisenhower in the early 1950s. The President sought to direct the country's efforts towards finding useful purposes for the use of radioisotopes and radiation science in general. At about this same time, other countries began their own food irradiation programs, with the goal of determining what the effect of this treatment would be on the wholesomeness, nutritional value, and safety of perishable foods. After extensive studies, the Office of the Surgeon General of the United States Army concluded in 1965 that foods irradiated with doses up to 56 kiloGrays were safe for human consumption. At the international level, a joint expert committee sponsored by the United Nations' Food and Agriculture Organization (FAO), the International Atomic Energy Agency (IAEA), and the World Health Organization (WHO) met during the 1960s and 70s. This committee was made up of scientists from around the globe, who spent a considerable time evaluating the results from the hundreds of scientific studies conducted on food irradiation during the past 20 years worldwide. Most of the studies included long-term multigenerational feeding of dogs, rats, and mice fed irradiation-sterilized meals. In 1980, this Joint Expert Committee concluded that irradiated foods are safe and wholesome.

Since then, there has been widespread approval and use of this technology throughout the world. There are several commercial irradiators operating in France, irradiating approximately 4 million tons of spices and seasonings, 7 million tons of poultry meat, and many other items. Japan irradiates approximately 15 to 20,000 tons of potatoes every year, and China irradiates several hundred tons of rice, as well as cigarettes. In all, there are over 20 countries that routinely irradiate some food commodity, with the United States irradiating approximately 5,000 tons of spices every year. It is important that we, both as consumers and as professionals, understand what this technology is all about, so that we can make a more educated decision on whether we support its use as a method of improving the safety of our food supply.

Radiation refers to the physical phenomenon in which energy travels through space or through matter, such as food. It is the process of applying this energy to a material to sterilize or preserve it. This is done by killing or otherwise inactivating the microorganisms, insects, and other pests that may contaminate the material. The type of radiation that is most useful for this purpose is "ionizing radiation". This form of radiation contains energy of such high levels that it causes the ejection of electrons from their orbitals, resulting in the formation of charged, or ionized, particles. Examples of radiation that is nonionizing are visible light, microwaves, and infrared radiation. The energy level of these forms of radiation is so low that ionization does not result, a necessary event for destruction of microbial contaminants in food.

The types of radiation that induce ionization can be found on the right side of the electromagnetic spectrum. These radiations have short wavelengths but have several million electron volts (MeV) of energy, and include gamma rays and x-rays. Gamma rays are produced by radioactive isotopes such as cobalt-60 and cesium-137 and contain energy of about 1 to 2 MeV. Electrons, although containing relatively low energy, can be accelerated with a linear accelerator or a Van de Graaff generator to achieve energy levels of 10 MeV and higher. These highly accelerated electrons can then be used to irradiate materials, such as food. Accelerated electrons can be converted to x-rays when they are made to collide with heavy metals such as tungsten.

The most important factor of the irradiation process is the dose that is to be applied to the product. The unit of measure of radiation in the International System of Units is the Gray (Gy), which is equal to the absorption of 1 joule of energy per kilogram of food. An older unit of measure still encountered in the literature is the rad, which equals 100 ergs of energy absorbed per gram of material. One Gray equals 100 rad, and thus 1 million rads (a Megarad) equals 10,000 Gray, or 10 kiloGray (kGy). Application of radiation may be divided broadly into three categories: high dose (>10 kGy), medium dose (1-10 kGy), and low dose (<1 kGy). At high doses food is essentially sterilized, just as can be done with commercial canning. At medium doses there is a "pasteurization" effect, where shelf life is extended and most pathogenic microorganisms are either destroyed or greatly reduced in numbers. At low doses the product is disinfested from insects and other higher forms of life, and ripening of fruits and vegetables is delayed.[12]

The dose a product is to receive is controlled by the time the food is exposed to gamma rays (the time the product is in the chamber) or by the speed of the conveyor which moves the product under the electron or x-ray beam. The longer the product is exposed to gamma rays the higher the absorbed dose, and the slower the product is moved under the electron or x-ray beam the higher the absorbed dose. The dose to be applied will affect foods differently, according to their composition. For instance, foods high in lipid content may become slightly rancid at doses that would not affect other products. Most of the effects of irradiation on the quality of foods is related to the formation of radicals by the ionization of oxygen, water, and lipid molecules in the food. One way to minimize these effects is to reduce the availability of these compounds so that radical formation is limited. This can be achieved by packaging the food under vacuum (thereby removing the oxygen) and by freezing the product (thereby reducing the amount of free water available for radical formation).

All irradiated foods must bear the "radura" symbol, signifying the treatment they have received. In the United States, the product label must also state that the product has been treated by ionizing radiation or by irradiation. This symbol was developed in the Netherlands and is internationally recognized by the World Health Organization and the International Consultative Group on Food Irradiation as the official symbol that indicates a product has been subjected to irradiation.

APPROVALS FOR FOOD IRRADIATION IN THE UNITED STATES

Approvals for this technology have been granted in many countries to varying degrees. In the United States, approval must be sought by petitioning the Food and Drug Administration, at which time evidence of scientific studies must be provided to the agency, substantiating the safety and wholesomeness of this process for a particular product. In 1963, the FDA approved the irradiation of wheat and wheat flour at doses between 0.2 and 0.5 kGy (20-50 krad) for insect disinfestation. Irradiation of white potatoes at doses between 0.05 and 0.15 kGy (5-15 krad) to inhibit sprouting was approved in 1964. In July 1983, the FDA approved irradiation doses of up to 30 kGy to control microbial contamination in dried spices and dehydrated vegetable seasonings. In June 1984, that approval was extended to cover insect disinfestation as well. In 1985 two additional uses were approved: irradiation of dried enzyme preparations at doses of 10 kGy and the treatment of pork carcasses and fresh pork cuts at doses between 0.3 and 1.0 kGy, excluding vacuum packaged products.

In May of 1990, the U.S. Food and Drug Administration issued a final rule to permit the safe uses of ionizing radiation for the control of food-borne pathogens in poultry. The ruling permits irradiation, up to 3 kGy on poultry (defined as any domesticated bird), fresh or frozen, and as whole carcasses, parts, or mechanically deboned. However, the poultry must be in a package that does not exclude air. In September 1992, USDA issued their final regulations on poultry irradiation. These rules imposed a minimum dose of 1.5 kGy and a maximum dose of 3.0 kGy. Labeling requirements are that the words "Treated with Radiation" or "Treated by Irradiation" and "Keep Refrigerated" or "Keep Frozen" must be on the label. In addition, a green radura symbol must be on the label. Currently there are petitions to the U.S. Food and Drug Administration for clearances of seafood and red meat for pathogenic bacteria control.

Irradiation Facilities

Food processors who are considering irradiation for their products are faced with a number of dilemmas. Some of these relate to the irradiation facilities and sources that can be used for irradiation. This chapter will discuss unique characteristics of irradiation facilities and sources and dosimetry.

FACILITIES

Presently, there are over 40 irradiation facilities that sterilize medical devices and supplies in the United States. In many instances, the design of food irradiators will be very similar to medical sterilization irradiators due to similar requirements for licensing the facilities. Food irradiators that are service-oriented facilities not dedicated to one product type or that are built in-line at a manufacturing plant will be similar to medical irradiators. However, food irradiation facilities will almost always have some large refrigeration capacity which is generally not found in medical irradiation facilities.

GENERAL FACILITY CHARACTERISTICS

All irradiation facilities have some common characteristics. These include an irradiation source, a biological shield, a product handling and transport system, an air evacuation system, and a safety and control system.[9] There are additional characteristics that may be included in an irradiation facility that depend on the type of source used in the facility or the types of products to be irradiated.

Irradiation sources that can be used for food irradiation are gamma rays produced from the decay of cobalt-60 or cesium-137, electron beams generated and accelerated to energies from 5 to 10 MeV by a machine, or x-rays from the collision of electrons, accelerated up to 5MeV, with a metal target.[3] Only gamma rays from cobalt-60 and accelerated electrons used directly are currently commercially available. A description of the sources will be presented later in this chapter.

A general design of a gamma irradiation facility is shown in Figure 1.1. The irradiation process area is surrounded by thick concrete barriers (walls, floor, and ceiling). These barriers serve as a biological shield so that gamma rays (or x-rays which are created in an electron beam facility when the electrons hit the walls or metal) cannot penetrate through the walls, floor, or ceiling to expose people to an irradiation dose. The biological shield is from 1.8 to 3 m (6 to 10 feet) thick if made with concrete. (Other materials such as lead can be used as a biological shield but generally, concrete is more economical.) The thickness depends on the energy of the irradiation source. Concrete 1.8 m (6 feet) thick is needed to shield gamma rays from a cobalt-60 source. Concretre 3 m (10 feet) thick is needed to shield a 10 MeV source that produces x-rays. The biological shield does not have to be one solid wall, but can be several walls whose thicknesses when added together equal the required thickness.

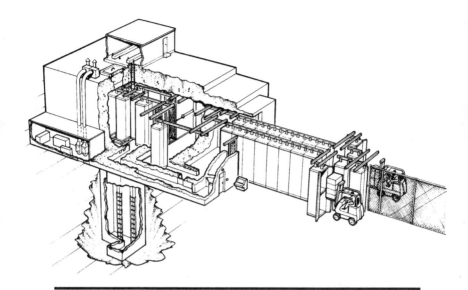

FIGURE 1.1. Commercial cobalt-60 irradiation facility: Automatic pallet irradiator. (Courtesy of Nordion International Inc., Kanata, Ontario, Canada)

The transport system is a critical component of the irradiation facility. Conveyor speed is the primary method for controlling the dose the product receives. Conveyor speeds need to be adjusted to compensate for changing dose rates of the source. In a gamma facility, the power of the cobalt-60 decays over time, and periodically some of the cobalt-60 is replenished in the facility, increasing the amount of gamma rays produced. This usually changes the dose rate of the source. In electron beam facilities, the e-beam machine can have a variable power selection which changes the amount of electrons generated and therefore the dose rate. In addition, conveyor speeds can be varied to achieve the different dosages that may be specified for different products.

To expose products to the irradiation source as a continuous process, the products are moved by a transport mechanism through a maze that has at least three 90 degree turns. The turns are required so that gamma rays or x-rays that may ricochet off walls can not leave the irradiation area and escape the biological shield. In gamma facilities, the transport is commonly an overhead conveyor with product carriers suspended from it. In electron beam facilities, the products are placed on a conveyor supported from the floor.

The area where products are loaded onto the conveyor before irradiation is usually physically separated by a fence from the area where the products are unloaded after irradiation. This is to prevent comingling of irradiated and nonirradiated products. Labeling and dosimetry, which will be discussed later, are also important in preventing nonirradiated products from being confused with irradiated products. Docks for unloading trucks of products to be irradiated are generally separated physically from docks used to load trucks with products that have been irradiated. Some deviation from this physical separation may occur in facilities that both manufacture and irradiate the product, such that the product is never labeled as being irradiated until after it has been irradiated.

A by-product of irradiation is ozone. Ozone forms when the gamma ray or electron ionizes oxygen molecules in the air, which combine to form ozone. The ozone must be removed from the irradiation chamber and not allowed to migrate out of the maze to the product handling area to expose people. Ozone is removed by an air evacuation system which draws outside air into the irradiation chamber and exhausts the ozone-contaminated air to the outside. To comply with environmental regulations, a large volume of air is needed to dilute the ozone to permissible levels. Additionally, the air handling system must be designed so that some of the exhausted air comes from the product handling area through the transport maze. This prevents any of the ozone from moving back through the maze and exposing workers in the facility. The concern about ozone extends into operating procedures. After the irradiation source is returned to a safe condition when operations are stopped, access to the irradiation chamber is delayed for several minutes to ensure that all of the ozone is evacuated before personnel enter the irradiation chamber.

The high volume of air that is used for ozone dilution makes it economically impractical to refrigerate the irradiation chamber. Hence, consideration of the time a refrigerated product resides in the irradiation chamber is important. Monitoring and recording product temperature before and after irradiation is required in inspection protocols. High-temperature climates may create a concern for temperature abuse of refrigerated products that reside in an irradiation chamber for extended times.

Safety systems are designed to prevent the accidental exposure of people to irradiation. While there can never be an absolute fail-safe system developed, there are some common techniques used to attain very safe operating conditions. These techniques include sensors, detectors, warning lights, and alarms. When not in operation, the irradiation source is placed in a condition such that people in the irradiation process area will not receive an irradiation dose. In a cobalt-60 facility, the source is stored in a deep water pool. In an electron beam facility, high voltage electricity is off. This is considered a "safe" condition.

Before an irradiation run, the irradiation chamber must be inspected by the operator to insure no person is in the chamber. During this inspection, flashing lights and audio alarms are activated. If someone were in the chamber, a cord located along all walls throughout the chamber could be pulled to prevent the facility from becoming operational. After the pre-operational checks have been completed successfully, the facility becomes operational. There is still a safety system, which is designed to return the irradiation source to a safe condition if there is an intrusion of the secured areas.

Placing the source in a safe condition means lowering the source rack into the water pool in a cobalt-60 facility, or shutting off high voltage in an electron beam facility. The conveyor systems are designed so that a person cannot ride into the irradiation chamber on the conveyor or enter the irradiation chamber maze in front or behind product carriers on the conveyor. Intrusion of the irradiation chamber maze is detected by electronic sensors on the access door, pressure mats on the floor, and by light curtains. Activation of any of these sensors or detectors causes the source to be returned to the safe condition.

GAMMA FACILITIES

Gamma facilities have several unique characteristics, including a water pool, a source rack, and a removable ceiling plug. There are also some operating procedures that are unique to gamma facilities. Licensing requirements for the facility and some of the operating protocols are administered through the Nuclear Regulatory Commission.

Gamma irradiation facilities have cobalt-60 as the source of irradiation. Cobalt-60 is obtained by exposing pure natural cobalt-59 pellets to a neutron source in a nuclear reactor to produce radioactive cobalt-60.[10] The cobalt-60 pellets are encased in double stainless steel cylinders, commonly called pencils. Nordion International, Inc.,[9] has a C-188 cobalt-60 pencil that is approximately 1.27 cm (.5 inch) diameter and 45 cm (17.75 inches) long. Each pencil has a different amount of gamma-producing power, measured as curies, depending on its age. At the time of manufacturing, a pencil can contain 6,000 to 13,000 curies. The number of curies in a pencil continually declines as the radioactive cobalt-60 decays. Many pencils are used in a gamma irradiation facility. The more pencils or, more accurately, curies a facility has, the greater the throughput capacity the facility will have. Commercial facilities generally would have over a million curies of cobalt-60.[8]

After the cobalt-60 pencils are produced, they are transported to the irradiation facility in a large lead-lined cask. The lead serves as the biological shield from the gamma rays that are being emitted. A cask can carry up to 200,000 curies of cobalt-60.[9] The casks are lifted from the transport truck and lowered into the irradiation facility. The facility has a ceiling plug that must first be removed. The plug is very massive because it serves as part of the biological shield of the facility. The cask is lowered through the ceiling opening into a large water pool. The water pool is about 6.7 m (22 feet) feet in depth. The large depth of the pool is needed because the pencils are removed from the cask inside the pool by the facility personnel standing above the pool, with the water serving as the biological shield for the personnel.

The pencils are gripped and held by long gripping devices and then placed into a metal source rack. Considerable training and practice is needed to adequately manipulate these devices under water. The source rack is a flat rack that generally is at least as tall and wide as the product carriers, and it may have several separate parts. The scheme for loading the pencils on the rack is carefully designed to place individual pencils at specific locations. The design takes into account the different curies of each pencil and the profile of the flux field of gamma rays that is desired.[10] For example, pencils with the lowest curies may be placed around the edges of the rack where the product dwells the least time, or concentrated on a separate rack that may be used for low-dose applications.

Gamma rays are produced continuously and are emitted in all directions from the cobalt-60 source. Since gamma rays are produced continually, efficient use of the source requires the product to be irradiated continually. When the source is stored in the water pool, it cannot irradiate any product yet gamma rays are still being produced. Minimizing downtime is important in maintaining efficient operations.

Gamma rays are emitted in all directions, which means that they cannot all be captured by the products being irradiated. The design of the product transport system needs to maximize the amount of gamma rays captured by the exposed products. The conveyor system is therefore designed to move products on both sides of the source rack.[10] Gamma rays penetrate very deeply. Even when a 1-m (40-inch) wide pallet of products is placed in front of the source rack, some of the gamma rays pass completely through the products. To capture more of those gamma rays, two or more rows of carriers are used. Therefore, the conveyor system in a gamma facility would have at least two tracks on both sides of the source rack.

There is minimal space between product carriers that are on the inner and outer conveyor tracks. This is so as to minimize the size of the irradiation chamber due to the cost of the concrete biological shield that surrounds the chamber. A larger irradiation chamber requires more concrete for the biological shield.[8] This cost must be balanced with the efficiency of more of the gamma rays being absorbed by the products, which requires multiple rows of carriers and hence a larger irradiation chamber.

Movement of the carriers on the conveyor system in the irradiation chamber is typically by a "shuffle and dwell" method. With this method, a carrier is moved to a position, held there for a period of time and then moved to the next position where it is held for another period of time. This process would continue until a carrier has occupied each position around the source rack. The speed at which the carriers are moved from one position to the next and the time each carrier dwells in the position depends on the dose the product is to receive and the number of curies in the source rack. Over time, the speed and dwell times are changed due to decay of the source or replenishment of the source.[10]

Generally, products are moved through the irradiation chamber very slowly. A carrier that enters the irradiation chamber would take several hours to pass through the chamber. However, carriers continually move into the chamber and out of the chamber, and because they can carry pallet loads of product, high throughputs can be achieved. Due to the long time required for the carriers to move through the irradiation chamber, which is not refrigerated, special insulated carriers or smaller product configurations on the carriers may be needed to ensure that a chilled product does not rise in temperature to an unacceptable level due to the warm air environment in the chamber. For irradiation of fresh meat or poultry, extensive temperature monitoring and recording is needed to document that the products are handled under acceptable conditions.

With multiple carriers moving through the irradiation chamber at a set speed and dwell time, any change in product types, sizes, or dose specification will likely cause a change in conveyor speed and/or dwell time. The last of a "lot" of products that enters the irradiation chamber must be moved through the chamber at the same speed and dwell time as the first of the "lot", and it must exit the irradiation chamber before a conveyor change is made. Hence, the chamber must be essentially emptied of one product type before a different product can be started through the chamber, which causes some inefficiencies in gamma facilities if significantly different products are irradiated consecutively.

ELECTRON BEAM FACILITIES

Some of the unique characteristics included in an electron beam facility are the need for circulating water with a heat exchanger for cooling, extensive electrical supplies, a vacuum system, and a reserve electrical generating capacity. These facilities and operations are generally regulated and licensed by state agencies that are responsible for x-ray facilities.

The irradiation source is an electron beam accelerator. The machine generates and accelerates electrons under vacuum. Due to the small mass that electrons have, they can not penetrate very deeply into a product. To be useful for food irradiation, electrons should be accelerated to energies of at least 5 million electron volts (MeV). The maximum energy approved for use in food is 10 MeV.[3] Higher-energy electrons have greater penetration into the product. However, at 5 MeV and irradiating from both sides of a product, the maximum thickness that can be penetrated is about 3.8 cm (1.5 inches). At 10 MeV, and with two-sided irradiation, the maximum thickness is about 8.9 cm (3.5 inches).[10] In addition, product densities can affect electron penetration. This will be discussed later in the chapter. Hence, accelerated electrons have limited applications in the type of products that can be irradiated. Since they cannot be used to irradiate pallet loads of products, they are more apt to be used as a part of the manufacturing line, before boxing and palletizing, when products are not likely to be too thick.

While electron energy determines the thickness that electrons can penetrate into a product, the number of electrons or power, measured in kilowatts (kW), determines the throughput. Compared to gamma sources, there is a greater efficiency in the utilization of electrons because they are directed at the product rather than emitted in all directions. Hence a 10 kW electron beam machine would have about the same irradiation power as a cobalt-60 source with about 1 million curies.[10] Because the power of electron beam accelerators is high, and the products are moved under the electron beam very rapidly, chilled products are exposed to ambient temperatures for only a brief time. Therefore, these products are less likely to have an unacceptable temperature rise.

There are several different types of electron beam accelerators that are used for many different industrial applications. For food irradiation, radio frequency (RF) linear accelerators are the type that can produce energies from 5 to 10 MeV and power from 10 to 50 kW.[7] As accelerator technology develops in the future, linear induction accelerators that have high-power output in the hundreds of kilowatts may come into commercial use.

To overcome the limitation of product thickness when accelerated electrons are used for irradiation, the electrons can be directed at a metal target to produce bremsstrahlung x-rays.[10] These x-rays can penetrate very thick products, just as can gamma rays. The yield of x-rays depends upon the atomic number of the metal in the target; tungsten and tantalum are most commonly used. Unfortunately, the yield of bremsstrahlung x-rays is very low, with throughput efficiencies being less than 8%. This is too low for x-rays to have throughputs similar to those of gamma facilities using the commercial electron beam accelerators currently available. Electron beam accelerators would need to have to have power levels of 200 kW or more to have throughput capacities similar to those of a cobalt-60 source of 1 million curies. One of the main problems in the production of bremsstrahlung x-rays is the generation of heat at the target. As development of high-power accelerators advances, improved target designs will be needed to avoid this.

High-energy and high-power electron beam accelerators generate heat during operation which can cause instability in the accelerator and a loss of power. To maintain the stability and power output of the accelerator, temperature must be maintained within a narrow range, requiring a large volume of circulating water that must be cooled and whose temperature must be tightly controlled to have less than 0.5°C (0.9°F) variation. Water cooling of some vacuum pumps is usually also connected to the same system.

Electrical failure or pump failure could cause an interruption of the water flow to the accelerator or vacuum pumps. With an electrical disruption the control system would immediately shut down the high voltage system so that generation of electrons would cease. However, overheating of the accelerator and vacuum pumps could briefly occur. Either of these failures could cause severe damage to the accelerator. To prevent damage, reserve pumps are put in-line to automatically start if the prime pump fails, and gas-fired electrical generators or battery packs are also available to supply reserve electrical power to water and vacuum pumps, if needed.

FACILITY COMPARISONS

While both types of facilities have many common characteristics because they result in ionizing radiation, the radiation sources reflect some differences in the operation of the facilities. There are differences in safety and malfunction procedures, maintenance procedures, product configuration, and operations.

A critical difference is that a cobalt-60 source can never be turned off. It must be transported, loaded into the facility and always handled with a biological shield to protect workers from exposure. There is a long history of safe use and handling of cobalt-60 in medical device sterilization facilities. In a gamma facility, when malfunctions trigger the irradiation chamber being placed in a safe condition, the source rack containing cobalt-60 must be mechanically returned to the storage pool. This takes a brief time and is subject to the possibility that the rack could become jarred or stuck above the storage pool.

There is possibility that a cobalt-60 pencil could become defective, and some of the cobalt-60 could escape from the pencil. Since cobalt-60 is not soluble in water, the released material can be isolated and vacuumed out of the water pool. An immovable source rack or a leaking pencil are rare events, but they are possibilities that can remedied, although with some difficulty. Since cobalt-60 decays, the number of curies in the source is constantly decreasing, so replenishment of the source is needed to maintain the desired throughput in the facility. Replenishment could occur as often as yearly, depending on a company's operating policy.

In an electron beam facility, electricity is the source generating electrons. Therefore, there is no inherent radioactivity in the facility and the machine can be transported and installed without a biological shield. Malfunctions trip electrical relays to the high-voltage source, causing electron generation to stop immediately. Electron beam machines have many systems that potentially could fail and result in a loss of operations. The electrical, water, and vacuum systems must all work correctly for the machine to operate. The electron beam is tuned and focused during acceleration. Beam stability depends on maintaining a constant temperature of the machine. Stray electrons can raise the temperature of the machine and cause a decrease in the vacuum below operating parameters. If machine temperature and vacuum are not maintained properly, the machine shuts down, interrupting production.

There is considerably more maintenance required in the various systems of a linear accelerator facility than is needed for a gamma facility. There are also some components, such as the electron generator, the RF generator, and the modulator, that have a finite useful life before they expire. It is probable that there are more service interruptions with an electron beam facility than with a gamma facility.

Sources

Gamma rays and x-rays are quite similar in their characteristics, but accelerated electrons are different in the way the exposed product absorbs a dose. Gamma rays and x-rays have no mass and can penetrate very deeply into a material. However, electrons, which have a small mass, are slowed as they enter a material, resulting in limited penetration.

ELECTRONS

Energy from accelerated electrons is absorbed as it enters the surface of the product. Due to their mass, electrons begin to slow down rapidly as they move through the product.[10] Even more energy is absorbed as the electrons slow down. The absorbed dose of irradiation energy, therefore, increases under the surface of the product. Then as the electrons move further into the product, the electrons move even more slowly with less and less energy being absorbed. If the product is too thick, the electrons will have lost all of their energy and can penetrate no further by the time they pass through the entire product.

Figure 1.2 shows the depth-dose distribution of electrons at two energy levels (5 and 10 MeV). Electrons with higher energy levels can penetrate into products to a greater depth. Regardless of the energy, Figure 1.2 depicts the absorbed dose increases as electrons enter the product. Notice that, after reaching a peak dose, the absorbed dose declines linearly. The absolute depth that electrons can penetrate into a product is relative to the density of the product.[10]

In Figure 1.2, the depth on the x-axis is in grams per square centimeter units which can be converted to units of thickness in centimeters by dividing by the density of the product (grams per cubic centimeter). For water, which has a density of one, the units for the x-axis in Figure 1.2 could be converted from grams per square centimeter to centimeters. Since most food products have a high water content, their densities will be close to one. However, some products and ingredients can have much lower densities than water. Therefore, electrons can penetrate much deeper in these products. There would only be a few ingredients and dried products that would have densities higher than water.

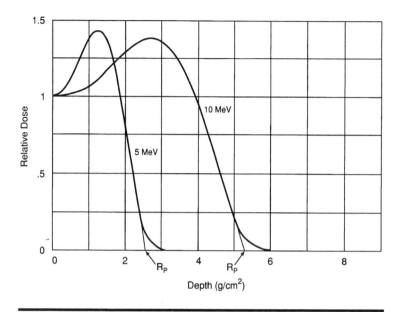

FIGURE 1.2. Electron depth-dose distribution. Note: The depth in g/cm^2 can be changed to product depth by multiplying by product density in g/cm^3.

An important consideration for penetration is with products that have varying densities, such as poultry with bones, or products that are in glass containers. Hence the dose-depth curves will only give an approximation of the depth that electrons can penetrate into a product.

The dose a product absorbs is measured in grays.[6] For food irradiation, doses in the kilogray (kGy) range are normally used. The dose on the y-axis of Figure 1.2 is in relative terms, because the dose is dependent on how slowly the product is moved through the electron beam, and on the power of the electron beam. The power of the beam does not influence the energy or the penetration of the beam into the product.

The penetration of the electrons at 5 or 10 MeV is not influenced by whether the product is receiving 0.5 kGy or 5 kGy of dose. The relative doses in Figure 1.2 also depict the variation in doses within the product. For example, if the dose at the surface of the product irradiated with 5 MeV electrons is 0.5 kGy, then the dose at the peak (1.25 g/cm^2) would be 0.7 kGy [(1.4 relative dose) × (0.5 kGy)]. Furthermore, if the surface dose was 5 kGy, then the peak dose would be 7 kGy, which is ten-fold greater in absolute dose than at a surface dose of 0.5 kGy.

The dose-depth curves in Figure 1.2 also show that when a product is irradiated, there is not just one dose the product absorbs, but a range of doses. There will always be a minimum and a maximum dose a product absorbs. For 10 MeV electrons, the lowest maximum and minimum (max./min.) dose ratio is at a depth of 3.8 cm (1.5 inches) (with a density of water, or 1) or less (Figure 1.2). With 5 MeV electrons, the lowest max./min. ratio is at a depth of 1.8 cm (.7 inch) or less. These depths are at the point where the dose at the bottom of the product is the same as at the surface of the product, and the max./min. ratio is about 1.4.

Products could be thicker than 3.8 cm (1.5 inches) (for 10 MeV) if the max./min. dose ratio specified for the product is greater than 1.4 (the lowest that can be achieved). Poultry has, by regulation, a minimum dose of 1.5 kGy and a maximum dose of 3.0 kGy. If the surface dose was 2.1 kGy then the maximum dose would be about 2.95 kGy and the dose at 4.2 gm/cm^2 would be about 1.6 kGy. Since boneless poultry has a density of about 0.95 gm/cm^3, the actual maximum thickness of the poultry would be 4.4 cm or about 1.75 inches if the poultry was irradiated from only one side.

The thickness could be more than doubled if the product is irradiated from both sides. Figure 1.3 shows the depth-dose distribution of 10 MeV electrons using two-sided irradiation. To attain a max./min. ratio of 1.4, the thickness of water would have to be 9.2 cm (3.6 inches) which is more than twice the thickness possible using one-sided irradiation. This occurs because the electrons at the low dosage areas are additive and therefore can be more completely used. However, thicknesses that are greater or less than the ideal thickness of 9.2 cm (3.6 inches) of water (9.7 cm [3.8 inches] of boneless poultry) will quickly change the max./min. ratio. Hence, a product like poultry could be irradiated with 10 MeV electrons from one side at thicknesses up to 4.4 cm (1.75 inches) or from two sides at thicknesses between 8.2 cm (3.25 inches) and 10.2 cm (4 inches).

The max./min. ratios would be too high at poultry thicknesses be-

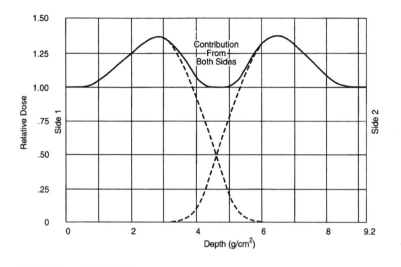

FIGURE 1.3. 10 MeV electron depth-dose distribution in water, using two-sided irradiation. Note: The depth in g/cm² can be changed to depth in cm by dividing by the density in g/cm³.

tween 4.4 cm (1.75 inches) and 8.2 cm (3.25 inches), or over 10.2 cm (4 inches) using 10 MeV electrons. Accelerating electrons to lower energies reduces the thickness at which a poultry product could be adequately irradiated. At 5 MeV, poultry would have to be less than 2.2 cm (0.9 inch) for one-sided irradiation, or between 3.8 cm (1.5 inches) and 4.8 cm (1.9 inches) for two-sided irradiation. At 7.5 MeV, the thickness is less than 2.8 cm (1.1 inches) (one-sided) or between 5.6 cm (2.2 inches) and 6.6 cm (2.6 inches) (two-sided). However, even with an electron beam accelerator that can operate at these three energy levels, there are still some thicknesses at which poultry could not be adequately irradiated, namely 4.8-5.6 cm (1.9-2.2 inches) and 6.6-8.2 cm (2.6-3.25 inches).

PHOTONS: GAMMA RAYS AND X-RAYS

Gamma rays and x-rays are photons that have some finite differences but in discussing their use in food irradiation they can be considered as the same. Compared to electrons, photon penetration into products is considerably deeper. Additionally, the absorbed dose from photons is highest at the surface and diminishes exponentially as they penetrate through the product.

For every incremental thickness of the product, the same percentage of photon energy is absorbed.[5, 10] The depth-dose distribution of photons in water is shown in Figure 1.4. The depth of penetration is determined by the density of the product being irradiated. With photons, the penetration depth is described in terms of half-thickness values which relate to the number of photons transmitted without loss of energy to the thickness of the product. With water, the half-thickness value

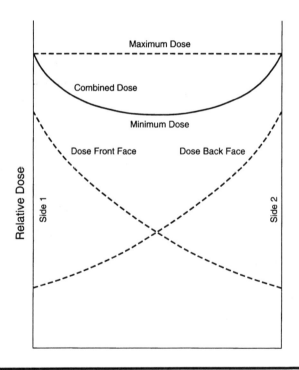

FIGURE 1.4. General x-ray or cobalt-60 depth-dose distribution in water for two-sided irradiation.

is 10.9 cm (4.3 inches), which means that at a depth of 10.9 cm (4.3 inches) 50% of the photons have not lost their energy and at a depth of 36.3 cm (14.3 inches) 10% of the photons have not lost their energy.

Because photons lose their energy exponentially, both sides of a product are always irradiated to attain a better max./min. ratio. The thinner the product the lower the max./min. ratio will be. In practice, the max./min. ratio specified for the product determines how thick the product can be. For example, irradiating packaged poultry to 1.5-3.0 kGy limits the thickness of the product to single boxes rather than pallets of boxes.

If approvals for irradiating poultry were up to 7 kGy as exists in many countries,[1] pallets of products could be irradiated much more economically. In photon irradiators, packages of products are commonly held in boxes, consisting of poultry packaged on trays, with the trays placed in the boxes to be irradiated. There can be a lot of air space between packages which must be taken into consideration when the thickness of the box is determined.

While penetration into products is nearly the same for both gamma rays and x-rays, production of x-rays is not currently an economical choice.[8] X-rays are produced by placing a metal target in the path of 5-MeV electrons (this is the highest electron beam energy permitted[5, 11]). A result of this collision is the production of x-rays with a broad spectrum of energies from 5 MeV to very low energies. However, another product of collision of electrons with the target is the production of a considerable amount of heat. This makes the efficiency of the target very low. Theoretically, production of x-rays would yield about 7% of the power of the electrons. However, in practice, this yield could be considerably less. Accelerators with power capacity of over 250 kW would be needed to approach the output of gamma facilities.

Dosimetry

When products are exposed to irradiation, chemical changes can occur. Free radicals are formed which are reactive and unstable. They interact with other food chemicals to form stable compounds called radiolytic products. These radiolytic products are not unique to irradiation in that other processes, such as cooking, produce radiolytic products. Hence, an irradiated product can not be differentiated chemically from a nonirradiated product, although considerable research is being conducted to be able to detect unique compounds in irradiated products.[2, 6, 10, 12]

Since there are no compounds in a product that can be used to determine the absorbed dose a product has received, a radiation sensitive material has to be irradiated along with the product. The radiation sensitive material, called a dosimeter, is measured to determine the absorbed dose. Hence, control of the irradiation process and compliance with dose regulations depends on having an accurate and reliable dosimetry system.

There are many different dosimeters that are used to determine a wide range of doses. For food irradiation where doses of less than 10 kGy are approved, only two dosimeter types have practical application as a routine process dosimeter; these are radiochromic films or plates and alanine.[5] The radiochromic dosimeters change color when irradiated and the amount of color change represents the amount of dose absorbed by the dosimeter. The color change is measured by a spectrophotometer set at a prescribed wave length. Alanine is an amino acid which, when exposed to irradiation, forms and retains free radicals. The free radicals, measured by electron spin resonance spectrometry, indicate the dose absorbed by the alanine pellet.

When dosimeters are irradiated, they change as a result, with that change being measured by an instrument. To relate that measurement to absorbed dose, a response curve of measurement signal and absorbed dose must be made. In an irradiation facility this response curve must be developed on site. A calibrated response curve is one where dosimeters of known absorbed dose are used to develop the response curve. The dosimeters of known absorbed dose must be traceable back to a national standard.[5] This is critical so that every irradiation processing facility can document that their calibrated response curve is linked to a national standard.

Calibration of dosimeters and traceability of the calibration to the national standard must be done very carefully. Fortunately, standard procedures have been developed for most dosimeters and for the different irradiation facilities. The standards have been developed by the

American Society of Testing and Materials, specifically by Committee E10.01.[3]

Dosimeters can be influenced by temperature, relative humidity, and light, and they can change over time.[5] Also, their weight or thickness can vary among dosimeters made from the same batch, and different batches of dosimeters can vary. Additionally, personnel and measurement instruments can induce some variation in the value of absorbed dose obtained. Therefore, selection of the type of dosimeter to use, and handling of dosimeters must be done with these potential variations in mind.

Dosimeters are used in the commissioning of a facility, in validation of the process for each product, and in measurement of absorbed dose distribution during a run. In commissioning a facility, a reference product is irradiated to determine the nonuniformity of the absorbed dose, which could lead to adjustments like redesigning the source plaque in a gamma facility or adjustments to centering controls in an electron beam facility until the level of nonuniformity is acceptable.[5] Usually the reference product is a stack of Plexiglas sheets with thin film dosimeters between the Plexiglas sheets. The reference product is positioned on the conveyor at locations where maximum and minimum doses would likely occur. The variation in the absorbed doses among the dosimeters creates a map of the nonuniformity of the dose distribution. When the level of nonuniformity is acceptable, then the facility becomes commissioned. The facility is periodically remapped with a reference product to determine any changes in the map of dose nonuniformity. The facility is also remapped if there are changes to the source, such as replenishment of cobalt-60 in a gamma facility or when changes or adjustments in components are made to an electron beam accelerator.

Validating an irradiation process for a product requires the placement of multiple dosimeters in various geometrical locations in the product to determine the maximum and minimum absorbed dose in the product during an irradiation process.[5, 12] Since an irradiated food will almost always have some maximum and minimum dose in the product specification, it is essential that a map of the dose distribution in the product is developed. If, during a validation trial of an irradiated product, the maximum or minimum absorbed dose lies outside the specification, then some changes are needed. Examples include reconfiguration of the product, alteration of the conveyor speed, reduction of power of the accelerator, and others. After these changes are made, then another validation trial is run to determine if the absorbed dose falls within the product specification. Once the irradiation process has been validated for that product, the dose-distribution map of the product is recorded for that product and is used to verify that when the same product is irradiated under the validated process, the absorbed dose of the product will fall within the specifications. Any change in the product or the source triggers the requirement to revalidate the process. During commercial irradiation, processing dosimeters are placed on the product periodically as a quality control check of the process. The absorbed dose of the quality control dosimeter will be referenced back to the dose-distribution of the validation map of the product.

Summary

Food processors considering irradiation as a treatment for their food products should consider whether to use a service facility to irradiate a portion of their products or whether to construct an irradiation facility as part of the processing line. Gamma facilities with a cobalt-60 source have advantages as a service facility due to the deep penetration of gamma rays into pallet size or near pallet size products. Service irradiation facilities are generally located some distance from a manufacturing plant, requiring products to be transported to the facility. It is a common practice that transported products are palletized for ease of handling. Due to the limited penetration of accelerated electrons, their use in irradiating products is optimized in consumer-ready packages which generally are thin enough for one- or two-sided irradiation. Electron beam sources have a higher dose rate, resulting in a faster process than in a gamma irradiator. The speed of the process could be important for foods held under refrigeration.

Control and verification of the irradiation process is dependent on the dosimetry system used in an irradiation facility. Dosimeters that can provide an accurate and stable response to irradiation under conditions in which the food product is irradiated are essential. Calibration of the dosimeters must be traceable to the national standard, and the validation of the irradiation process for each food product must documented. Since the irradiated product can not be tested definitively as being irradiated to the specified absorbed dosage range, dose-distribution mapping is critical for documenting compliance with the irradiation specifications.

References

1. Anonymous. 1991. Food Irradiation Newsletter. Joint FAO/IAEA Division of Nuclear Techniques in Food and Agriculture, International Atomic Energy Agency, Vienna, Austria.

2. Anonymous. 1977. Irradiation Dosimetry, Techn. Report, Series 178, International Atomic Energy Agency, Vienna, Austria.

3. ASTM. 1994. Annual Book of ASTM Standards, Nuclear (II), Solar and Geothermal Energy, Vol. 12.02, American Society of Testing and Materials, Philadelphia, Pennsylvania.

4. CAST. 1989. Ionizing Energy in Food Processing and Pest Control: II. Applications. Report No. 115. Council for Agricultural Science and Technology, Ames, Iowa.

5. McLaughlin, W.L., A. W. Boyd, J. C. McDonald, K. H. Chadwick and A. Miller. 1989. Dosimetry for Radiation Processing. Taylor and Francis, London.

6. McLaughlin, W.L., R. D. Jarrett,Sr., and T. A. Olejnik. 1982. Dosimetry. In: Preservation of Food by Ionizing Radiation, Vol 1, E. S. Josephson and M. S. Peterson, Eds. CRC Press, Boca Raton, Florida.

7. MeV Industries, SAINT-AUBIN Cedex, France.

8. Morrison, R.M. 1989. An Economic Analysis of Electron Accelerators and Cobalt-60 for Irradiating Food, Technical Bulletin No. 1762, Economic Research Service, U.S. Department of Agriculture, Washington D. C.

9. Nordion International Inc., Corporate Offices, Kanata, Ontario, Canada.

10. Woods, R. J., and A. K. Pikaev. 1994a. Radiation: Sources and Characteristics. In: Applied Radiation Chemistry: Radiation Processing. John Wiley and Sons, Inc., New York, New York.

11. Woods, R.J., and A.K. Pikaev. 1994b. Radiation treatment of food. In: Applied Radiation Chemistry: Radiation Processing. John Wiley and Sons, Inc., New York, New York.

12. Woods, R.J., and A. K. Pikaev. 1994c. Radiation Dosimetry. In: Applied Radiation Chemistry: Radiation Processing. John Wiley and Sons, Inc., New York, New York.

C H A P T E R   2

MICROBIOLOGY OF IRRADIATED FOODS

ELSA A. MURANO, PhD

Introduction

In learning about how food irradiation can benefit consumers, it is important that we begin with an understanding of why this process should be used at all. What are its benefits, its shortcomings, and its usefulness for both consumers and the food industry? Claims are made that this process will extend the shelf life of perishable foods and make food safer to eat. How this is possible is largely through the ability of food irradiation to eliminate microorganisms from foods. Some of these organisms are responsible for spoiling our food, some are used to manufacture desirable and healthful products, and some are responsible for causing disease. In order to understand how the process of food irradiation can really benefit consumers, it is necessary to discuss some facts regarding these tiny beings. Following is a summary that will introduce the reader to the subject of food microbiology, as well as explain how irradiation affects these creatures. It is not highly technical, as the intended readers are assumed to have very little knowledge of this subject. However, it should provide the necessary information to understand the impact that microorganisms have on our food supply, and the contributions that food irradiation can make to maintain its safety. For more information on the topics covered in this introduction, several excellent textbooks on microbiology and food microbiology are presented at the end of this chapter.

THE MICROBIAL WORLD

Microorganisms are, in the simplest sense, living things too small to be viewed by the naked eye. They are found everywhere: lakes and streams, soil, plants, animals, and air. Most require the same conditions for survival as we do: moderate temperatures, plenty of oxygen and water, and neutral pH. Some, however, are able to survive in the harshest of environments, such as the high-temperature hydrothermal vents deep in the ocean, the driest deserts, and under the permafrost of the tundra. Their primary function in nature is that of self-perpetuation, and thus they utilize available nutrients in the form of organic matter, converting them to energy and inorganic compounds such as nitrate. In doing so, microorganisms form part of the cycle of life, with their waste products being utilized by plants, which are in turn consumed by animals. Both plants and animals then serve to provide microorganisms with a source of nutrients for growth in the form of carbohydrates, proteins, lipids, etc.

The term "microorganism" is used to refer to bacteria, yeasts, molds, and viruses, with these life forms differing from each other in very fundamental ways. Yeasts and molds belong to the kingdom Fungi, whereas bacteria are members of the kingdom Protista. Viruses are not true organisms in the sense that they are not cellular. In fact, some scientists believe that viruses may not be "alive", since they are not able to reproduce by themselves. They need to use the mechanisms of the host cell which they are invading in order to replicate, a characteristic that makes viruses true parasites of the microbial world. The names of microorganisms are in Latin, which adds to the consternation that some students feel when they first become acquainted with the field. The first word in the name refers to the genus to which the organism belongs, and the second word refers to the species within that genus. Most anybody who has taken a biology course has come across the organism *Escherichia* (genus) *coli* (species). We will begin by discussing the role of bacteria in the natural world.

BACTERIA

Bacteria are the most commonly found microorganisms in nature. They can be classified in three groups: (1) "useful" bacteria, (2) "spoilage" bacteria, and (3) "pathogenic" bacteria. The useful organisms are those that are able to produce desirable products due to their ability to ferment sugars. Common examples are the organisms that ferment milk to produce cheese, butter, sour cream, and yogurt, as well as those that ferment grain products to yield ethanol. In addition, useful bacteria can be added to foods for health purposes. One common example is milk that has been "spiked", or inoculated, with *Lactobacillus acidophilus*. Addition of this organism allows lactose-intolerant consumers to drink the milk, since the organism takes care of breaking down the sugar lactose before it reaches the digestive tract of the individual. The second group of bacteria, the "spoilage" bacteria, are most commonly associated with the undesirable changes in odor, color, flavor, and texture or appearance of food. The organism *Leuconostoc mesenteroides* is known for its ability to form a slime layer in certain refrigerated foods, a decidedly undesirable characteristic of long-stored frankfurters.

The third class of bacteria, the "pathogenic", or disease-causing, is responsible for most of the outbreaks of food-borne illness in the United States. Most consumers are familiar with outbreaks involving *Salmonella enteritidis* in eggs, *Clostridium botulinum* in home-canned vegetables, and *Escherichia coli* serotype O157:H7 in ground beef.

Bacteria are unicellular organisms, basically classified into two major groups, Gram positive and Gram negative, depending on whether they can retain Crystal Violet stain within their membrane after the Gram staining procedure. Within this classification, they are grouped according to shape as bacilli (rod shaped), cocci (round shaped), or spirilli (spirally shaped). Most bacteria exist as "vegetative cells", actively growing and multiplying as long as environmental conditions and availability of nutrients permit it. Some bacteria, however, have the ability to form "spores", a characteristic that can be very useful for these organisms. These structures enable sporulating bacteria to survive harsh conditions where water and nutrients may not be available, or where the temperature is not conducive to growth. Bacteria that are able to sporulate are often found in the most severe environments, an example of which is *Bacillus thuringiensis*. While in the spore stage, these organisms are basically dormant, not able to grow or multiply. Upon subsequent exposure of the spores to environmental conditions suitable for growth, to the presence of a specific compound, or to a sudden heat treatment, the spores germinate, becoming vegetative cells once again, growing and multiplying as the conditions permit it.

YEASTS AND MOLDS

Yeasts exist mostly as single cells, although they can occur as single cells loosely aggregated into filaments called "hyphae". Just as some bacteria form spores under undesirable environmental conditions, some yeasts can form four spores in a sac, called "ascus" when nutrients are not available. These spores germinate when nutrients are supplied, giving rise to new cells that can reproduce. Unlike bacteria, which reproduce by fission of a cell into two, yeasts reproduce by "budding". In this process, the daughter cell appears as a small protrusion in the original cell that gradually enlarges. This "bud" eventually separates from the original cell and goes on to grow and multiply in the same way as its parent did. The most common yeast belongs to the genus *Saccharomyces*, used in the baking and brewing industries for its ability to form gas and alcohol.

Molds can be either unicellular or multicellular. They are found in decaying organic matter and grow in the form of a tangled mass that spreads rapidly and may cover several inches in 2 to 3 days. The mass is referred to as "mycelium", and it is composed of many filaments, or "hyphae". The mycelia serve to anchor molds to surfaces, and it is thought that they are used to transfer nutrients from one portion of the mold to another. Some molds are termed "useful" because they produce substances that can be used to kill bacteria. The antibiotic penicillin, well known for its contribution in minimizing bacterial infections, was discovered when Alexander Fleming noticed how a Petri plate containing a bacterial culture showed an area with no bacterial colonies. This area of the plate had been contaminated with a mold, and it was by production of penicillin by this mold that growth around the mold colony by bacteria had been inhibited. Some useful molds produce certain compounds that contribute to the flavor of some food products. Most notably, *Penicillium roqueforti* is the organism responsible for giving blue cheese its characteristic flavor and odor. Just as with bacteria, there are pathogenic molds. These produce chemicals called "toxins", and are usually associated with grains. An example is *Aspergillus flavus*, a mold which produces aflatoxin, known to cause liver disease upon ingestion, and to induce cancer when consumed over time.

VIRUSES AND OTHER PARASITES

Viruses are obligate parasites, and are among the strangest of living things. They cannot live outside a host cell, which makes it difficult to isolate them in the laboratory. These organisms are fairly "host-specific", usually being particular about the type of cell they invade. Viruses are curious entities in that they are considered inert when not associated with a host. They are not cells in the true sense, and are often named by the disease they cause or where they were first discovered, rather than by genus and species. Viruses in a bottle sitting on the shelf would not be expected to grow, and in fact, viruses found in foods do not grow at all while on the food. However, even after years of storage, if they come in contact with a living host such as a human being, the virus can invade the tissue and cause disease. Viruses act by injecting their genetic material into the host cell. This material gets assimilated into the host genetic material, enabling the virus to use the host's mechanisms to replicate. There are no "spoilage" viruses since they do not grow in food. However, some viruses can infect bacteria and use them as a host. If the useful bacteria in a food product are destroyed by such a virus, then spoilage bacteria can take over and flourish without competition for nutrients. Thus, viruses can be indirect spoilers.

There are other parasites associated with food, which like viruses, do not grow in food but are responsible for outbreaks of food-borne illness. The most common are the protozoa, like *Toxoplasma gondii*, the flatworms *Taenia saginata* (beef tapeworm) and *Taenia solium* (pork tapeworm), and the roundworms like *Trichinella spiralis*. These are not usually considered microorganisms, since their forms can be seen with the naked eye. Protozoa occur in cysts which take residence in muscle tissue after ingestion of food contaminated with them. The flatworms do not have a body cavity, and depend on the digestive mechanism of the human host for all nourishment. They reproduce by laying eggs in soil, which are then ingested by cattle. The roundworms burrow into muscle tissue of the host, where they can remain for up to 10 years in a calcified state.

WHERE MICROORGANISMS ARE FOUND

As stated before, microorganisms are truly ubiquitous: they are found everywhere. They can be associated with soil, from which they can enter the atmosphere by the wind and be deposited in bodies of water and the soil by rain. Microbial density is highest on the surface of soil and water, with growth being limited to areas where organic matter can be found (plant roots, feces, etc.). Contamination of food by the soil can occur by direct contact in the case of root crops and tubers, or by the mechanical action of harvesting, where the machinery churns the soil and mixes it, and all its contaminants, with the crop being harvested. In addition to contact with soil, water can be contaminated by contact with waste matter. It can then contaminate food through direct contact, as with seafood found in contaminated waters, or crops irrigated with water containing microorganisms. Since water is one of the ingredients in most foods, contaminants it may harbor can spread rather quickly. Organisms that become airborne by gusts of wind contaminate the atmosphere, with air near the earth being more highly contaminated than air at higher altitudes, and air over land being more contaminated than air over oceans. To control the microbial load in a processing plant, positive pressure is often used, in which air flows out of the room to avoid introducing air from the outside into the plant environment. Humans and animals are perhaps the most important reservoirs of microbial contaminants. We have bacteria on the surface of the skin, on mucus membranes, the nasal cavity, the mouth, and the intestinal tract. The importance of hand washing can never be overestimated when one considers that millions of microorganisms, some of which are pathogenic, lurk in our fecal material!

HOW MICROORGANISMS GROW

Arguably, there is no subject more important to the food industry than that of understanding microbial growth. It is important since, in knowing what the best conditions for growth are, we can optimize fermentation reactions in food manufacture and enumerate microorganisms more rapidly. Similarly, if we know the conditions that are worst for microbial growth, we can utilize this information in devising a strategy for the reduction or elimination of pathogens or undesirable microorganisms in foods.

Bacterial growth can be described in simplistic terms as a three-part process, the first part being when the cells are active, metabolically speaking (that is, they are using nutrients, but are not dividing). This is typically called the "lag" phase of growth. In the second phase, the cells have become accustomed to the surroundings and are actively multiplying, usually once every 20 minutes under the best conditions. The growth is exponential, or logarithmic, in that one cell becomes two, two become four, four become eight, eight become sixteen, sixteen become thirty-two, and so on. This is called the "log" phase of growth. In the third phase, the cells are beginning to run out of nutrients, and the amount of waste being produced by the cells themselves is approaching levels toxic to the bacteria. In this phase, the number of cells dividing is roughly the same as the number of cells dying. This is called the "stationary" phase of growth. After this, more cells die than are produced, resulting in death of the culture. When the overall conditions for growth are optimal, the time needed for cells to go from the lag to the stationary phase is relatively short, whereas the time increases if the conditions are less than ideal.

WHAT MICROORGANISMS NEED TO GROW

There are several requirements for microorganisms to flourish: availability of nutrients, moisture content, acidity, oxygen content, and temperature of the environment. Nutrient requirements consist of a carbon source, a nitrogen source, and growth factors such as vitamins and minerals. The carbon source is usually in the form of sugars, and the nitrogen source is protein broken down to amino acids or a nitrogen-containing compound such as ammonia. The carbon source is used to generate energy for the cell to carry out its metabolic processes, while the nitrogen source is used to synthesize proteins and enzymes needed for building new cells and maintaining existing ones. Not all organisms need to obtain vitamins and minerals, since there are bacteria that can manufacture some of these components themselves. It is obvious that the food we eat is full of just the kinds of compounds needed by microorganisms to grow. It is also easy to see that the composition of a particular food can play a role in the types of microorganisms that will grow in it.

Water is used by the microbial cell to bring in nutrients and to dispel wastes to the outside world. Water is also necessary for chemical reactions, such as those involved in metabolizing sugars, genetic replication, etc. In foods, water can be either free or bound. In the free form, it is available for microorganisms to use in the processes described above. In the bound form, water is held by physical forces to macromolecules in the food (sugars, proteins, etc.), and thus it is not available for microorganisms. Free water is expressed in terms of water activity (Aw), with the maximum water activity a food can have being equal to 1.0, which is the water activity of pure water. Most spoilage bacteria have a Aw requirement of at least 0.9, with some exceptions. The most notable exception is *Staphylococcus aureus*, an organism found in cured meat products, which can grow in as low as 0.85 Aw. Yeasts can grow at a Aw as low as 0.87, with osmophilic yeasts being able to tolerate 0.60. As a rule, molds are more tolerant of low Aw than bacteria and most yeasts, with a minimum Aw requirement of 0.70. It is not surprising that foods of low Aw, such as jams, hard cheeses, and cakes, are spoiled by molds while foods of high Aw, such as meat and dairy products, are spoiled by bacteria.

Acidity of a food is expressed in terms of the pH scale, with a pH of 1.0 being the lowest (representing the most acidic), a pH of 7.0 being neutral, and a pH of 14.0 being the highest (representing the most alkaline). Human blood has a pH of approximately 7.0, with most bacteria having their optimum pH for growth at that level. Some bacteria, like those used in fermentation reactions, can tolerate pH levels of 4.0, while others found in aquatic environments can tolerate up to 8.6. As with water activity, yeasts and molds are more tolerant of extremes of pH than most bacteria, with yeasts growing in a pH as low as 3.0 and as high as 8.5, and molds in a pH as low as 2.0 and as high as 11.0. With such an advantage over bacteria, it would stand to reason that bacteria would never be able to compete with yeasts and molds for nutrients.

This is true at extremes of pH, but at pH of 6.5 to 7.5 bacteria outgrow yeasts and molds, and it is this speed of multiplication that enables them to out compete their adversaries. Most foods fall in the range of neutral to slightly acidic pH, with seafood being the most alkaline meat product. Fruits are usually acidic, with pH ranging between 1.8 and 4.2, and for this reason their spoilage is usually due to molds and not bacteria. The most alkaline foods in nature are egg whites, with a pH of 7.6 to 9.5. Foods that are low in acid (pH above 4.6) are made commercially sterile by heating under pressure, since the pH is not low enough to prevent the growth of pathogenic microorganisms. Foods that are high in acid (pH below 4.6) do not need to be processed in this way since the pH is low enough to prevent growth of pathogens.

Microorganisms can be classified according to their tolerance of oxygen. Strict aerobes need atmospheric levels of oxygen to survive (20% O_2), while facultative anaerobes can grow both in the presence and absence of oxygen, even though they grow best when oxygen is available. Microaerophilic organisms cannot tolerate the full complement of oxygen found in the atmosphere, but still need it to survive. Levels of 6% O_2 have been found to be optimum for growth of these cells. Strict anaerobes cannot tolerate the presence of oxygen at all, since it is toxic to them. Such microorganisms need to be kept in a vacuum or in the presence of other gases, such as nitrogen or carbon dioxide. Bacteria can be in any of these categories, while yeasts and molds are basically aerobic organisms.

Scientists have found organisms that survive temperatures nearing the boiling point of water (98°C or 208.4°F), as well as below the freezing point (−15°C or 5°F). However, most microorganisms require much milder temperatures for growth. Psychrophilic organisms are those that like temperatures below 20°C (68°F), while psychrotrophic organisms are those that can tolerate such low temperatures, but prefer higher temperatures for optimum growth. Both of these groups include some spoilage and some pathogenic organisms. Mesophilic organisms are those that grow at temperatures between 30 and 40°C (86 and 104°F), and they include most pathogenic bacteria, as well as most spoilage organisms. Finally, thermophilic organisms are those that prefer high temperatures (above 55°C or 131°F) and include only spoilage organisms. The closer the temperature of a food product is to the optimum growth temperature of a particular microorganism, the faster the organism will grow (the shorter it will take for the cells to divide). Thus, one can use the doubling or generation time to calculate the shelf life of a particular food product, or time it will take for the product to spoil. It is no wonder that refrigeration is the oldest form of food preservation, when one considers how it can slow down the growth, or doubling time, of most spoilage and pathogenic microorganisms.

Given the information presented here on the factors that affect the growth of microorganisms, one can begin to devise ways in which foods can be preserved by simply manipulating some of these factors. For instance, a product with a Aw below 0.8 would not support the growth of most bacterial pathogens. However, if spores are present they may well survive this Aw and remain viable as a potential threat to the safety of the consumer. To counteract this, one may choose to lower the pH of the product to below 4.6, which is known to prevent bacterial spore germination. Such is the case with fermented dry sausages. If the desired product must have a high Aw, then a heating step can be added, in which the product could be rendered commercially sterile and shelf-stable, which is in fact what is done in commercial canning of low-acid foods. However, this may not be acceptable if one desires a product that is as fresh as possible. Thus, one may heat the product to medium temperatures to eliminate most pathogens, in which case the product needs to be refrigerated to slow down the growth of microorganisms. But what if the product needs to be sold fresh (uncooked), but the threat of microbial contaminants needs to be reduced or eliminated? This is where the technology of irradiation can serve to yield a product that is fresh, has a high Aw and neutral pH, but is devoid of pathogenic microorganisms.

FOOD-BORNE ILLNESS

Much has been written regarding the impact that food-borne illness has on our society, from the medical as well as from the economic perspectives. Outbreaks have been caused by consumption of practically every type of food commodity, from meats to eggs, dairy products, fruits, vegetables, and seafood. The cost has been said to approach the billions of dollars, when one considers medical costs, insurance costs, and time lost from work.[51] Even so, there is speculation that only 10% of all food-borne illness cases are ever reported, with most patients choosing not to see a physician, allowing the illness to run its course.[2] It is important for the food industry, as well as academia and regulatory agencies, to come to an agreement to determine the steps that need to be taken in order to minimize or eliminate such occurrences. The first step is understanding the enemy, and thus, the following summary is presented as an introduction to this topic.

Bacteria, although not the only cause, are the leading cause of food-borne illness in the United States (Table 2.1).

Bacteria cause disease by three basic mechanisms: invasion, intoxication, or intoxification. Invading bacteria usually need to exist in large numbers in the food (10,000 organisms per gram) for them to result in illness of the individual consuming the food. This is because the larger the number of cells being ingested, the higher the probability of some cells surviving the acidic conditions of the human stomach, and of reaching their ultimate destination: the small intestine. However, this is not a hard rule, since there have been cases where the food associated with an illness contained fewer than 100 cells per gram.[5] Once invading bacteria reach the intestinal tract, they begin to colonize the tissue, which can take 12 to 36 hours. An example of such an organism is *Salmonella typhimurium*, the causative agent of salmonellosis from consumption of contaminated poultry and other fresh meats. This organism acts by damaging the mucosa, or lining of the small intestine. This results in fluid from the mucosa being released into the lumen of the small intestine, resulting in diarrhea. If the cells invading the tissue cause ulceration of the intestine, diarrhea with blood can result. Some organisms

Table 2.1. **Annual average number of food-borne disease outbreaks by causative agent**

Causative Agent	Outbreaks	
	Number	Percent
Bacterial	120.0	66.0
Chemical	46.4	25.5
Parasitic	7.2	4.0
Viral	8.2	4.5

Source: Adapted from CAST.[5]

can eventually penetrate the capillaries adjacent to the intestinal cells, enabling the bacteria to reach the blood and, through it, the rest of the body.

Intoxications are caused by consumption of food containing toxin produced by microorganisms. These toxins can affect the ability of intestinal tract cells to absorb nutrients and water from the food we eat. In disrupting this mechanism, they force secretion of water into the lumen of the small intestine, resulting in diarrhea, as with invading bacteria. Toxin is usually produced by the microorganism in the food product itself. There is very little waiting before the onset of symptoms, since the toxin usually reaches the intestines a few minutes after ingestion. Examples of such toxin-producers are *Staphylococcus aureus* and *Clostridium botulinum*. *S. aureus* produces seven types of enterotoxin (or toxin that affects the intestinal tract). The toxins are heat-stable, thus heating from normal cooking does not inactivate them, with a temperature of 100°C (212°F) for 30 minutes being reported as necessary for complete inactivation. The symptoms of the disease are nausea, vomiting, diarrhea, and cramps with prostration. The fact that the symptoms develop in as few as 2 to 4 hours after ingestion is typical of toxin-producing organisms. *C. botulinum* produces a different type of toxin, termed a "neurotoxin". This chemical is produced in the food and, upon consumption, it causes botulism by interfering with the mechanism that sends nerve impulses to the muscles of the body. Symptoms include blurred vision, difficulty in swallowing and speaking, and paralysis of the involuntary muscles which ultimately can lead to death from asphyxiation. The toxin is the most potent natural substance known to man, with only a few nanograms being necessary to cause disease.

Finally, intoxifications are the result of consuming a food product contaminated with a bacterial pathogen. After the cells reach the intestines, they begin to produce toxin inside the body. The time elapsed from the time of ingestion to the development of symptoms is usually longer than for intoxications. An example of an organism that grows in the food and produces toxin once inside the body is *Clostridium perfringens*. Upon ingestion of food contaminated with this bacterium, the cells attach to the intestinal tract, where they sporulate. It is believed that the spore coat is the toxin. Symptoms include watery diarrhea and acute abdominal cramps.

Molds cause disease by producing highly toxic substances called "mycotoxins". Most molds are found in cereal grains such as rye, wheat, barley, and oats, and in feed grains like corn and soybeans. Some mycotoxins cause severe conditions like gangrenous ergotism, where the patient feels a burning sensation in the feet and hands that ultimately develops into loss of circulation and gangrene with the loss of limbs as a result. Others, such as aflatoxin, can cause liver necrosis when consumed in medium quantities, and liver cancer when consumed in low quantities over a long period of time. Since molds are easily inhibited by the exclusion of oxygen, it has been a common practice in the industry to package products suspected of having mold in vacuum or modified atmospheres containing nitrogen or CO_2 gas.[4]

In the case of viruses, illness is primarily caused by infection of the host intestinal tract cells with the virus. A virion (virus particle) can replicate inside a tissue cell and remain there for some time while more virions are produced. The host cell is then lysed and the virions are released into the surrounding tissue, ready to infect more cells. Symptoms include vomiting and diarrhea, which usually runs its course in 1 or 2 days. The virus particles are shed in the feces, which can then be a source of contamination.

Effect of Irradiation on Microorganisms

HOW IRRADIATION KILLS MICROBIAL CELLS

Food irradiation is simply a process in which energy of high level is used to ionize a material, in this case food. Ionization takes place because gamma rays, x-rays, or accelerated electrons (depending on the source of radiation) are able to eject electrons from chemical bonds, thus disrupting the structure of molecules.[6] If the molecule is DNA (deoxyribonucleic acid), which is the cell's genetic code that allows it to multiply, the consequences can be devastating. This is in fact the primary mechanism by which irradiation destroys microorganisms: by breaking bonds on the DNA molecule, thereby rendering the cells unable to replicate. It must be noted that scientists have calculated that irradiation will break 6 chemical bonds for every 10 million bonds present in a system.[7] This is certainly a small proportion, but when you consider that any change in the DNA molecule can adversely affect how genes will be coded and duplicated, not many bonds need to be broken to have an impact on the microbial cell.

The result is that, because of irradiation, microbial cells can be easily and quickly destroyed, leaving them unable to replicate, transport and metabolize nutrients, and grow. Thus, by destroying spoilage microorganisms, foods can become longer lasting, and by destroying pathogens foods can become safer. Destruction of microorganisms by irradiation is logarithmic, that is, if a certain dose destroys 10 cells of a particular organism in a particular food, twice that dose will destroy 100 cells, three times the dose will destroy 1,000 cells, and so on. This is important in that one can predict the dose that will be needed to destroy a certain number of organisms in a food, enabling food processors to design the process so that all cells of a particular organism are killed, building into the equation a margin of 2 or 3 decimal reductions to ensure that the product is free of that organism.

FACTORS AFFECTING DESTRUCTION OF MICROORGANISMS

Destruction of microorganisms by irradiation is affected by several factors. First and foremost, microorganisms differ in their sensitivity to irradiation, depending on morphological variations, just as they differ in their sensitivity to heating, drying, and freezing. Viruses are usually more resistant than spores of bacteria, which are more resistant than vegetative cells of bacteria, which are more resistant than yeasts and molds. In fact, a good rule of thumb is that the more simple the lifeform, the more resistant it is to irradiation. This holds true in the case of parasites versus microorganisms, with the former being more sensitive to irradiation than the latter. It is not surprising that, even though it takes a dose as high as 40 kGy to destroy viruses, it only takes 0.01 Gy to kill a human being.[39] Resistance to irradiation is expressed as the "D value", or dose required to reduce the microbial population in a given medium (or food) by 10-fold. Thus, an organism with a D value of 0.5 kGy is more resistant to irradiation than one with a D value of 0.25 kGy, since it takes a dose twice as large to destroy the same number of cells in the population.

Another factor that affects the survival of microorganisms to irradiation is that of temperature: the lower the temperature the higher the D value. *Yersinia enterocolitica*, which normally has a D value of approximately 0.2 kGy in ground beef irradiated at 25°C (77°F), has a D value of about 0.4 kGy when irradiated in ground beef at −30°C (−22°F).[13] It has been suggested that the reason this occurs is that at lower temperatures the indirect antimicrobial effect of radical formation is diminished. Since water is not as available when the temperature drops, especially below freezing, not as many radicals are formed and thus it takes a higher dose to destroy the cells. Interestingly, this temperature effect is not seen when the microbial cells are in a simple medium, with no difference in survival of *Campylobacter jejuni* cells being seen when the cells are exposed to irradiation in broth at 30°C vs.−30°C (86°F vs. −22°F).[25]

The composition of the medium in and of itself also has an impact on the susceptibility of microorganisms to irradiation. The D value of *Listeria monocytogenes* was calculated to be 0.35 kGy when irradiated in a bacteriological medium (BNT), compared with a value of 0.77 kGy in chicken.[22] Finally, the atmosphere in which the product is packaged for irradiation seems to affect survival of the cells, although exactly how is a subject of debate. In one study, scientists found that irradiation of poultry under vacuum or packaged in CO_2 had the most lethal effect on *Salmonella*, *E. coli*, and *Lactobacillus*, compared with meat packaged in air.[33] However, other investigators reported that chicken irradiated at 2.5 kGy showed no difference in the number of survivors immediately after irradiation in meat packaged in air vs. vacuum.[54] The possible effect of atmosphere on survival of microorganisms to irradiation is further discussed in a later section (Combination of Irradiation with Other Processes).

Similar effects regarding temperature and medium composition on elimination of microorganisms other than bacteria by irradiation have been observed. Inactivation of human immunodeficiency virus (HIV) by gamma irradiation was affected by temperature: with the lower the temperature the higher the dose needed to inactivate the same number of virions in liquid vs. frozen plasma.[21] Irradiation of various sodium phosphate solutions of pH ranging from 5.0 to 6.2 showed no significant difference in survival of *Penicillium cyclopium*.[3] In a study involving irradiation of maize containing the yeasts *Phycomycetes* and *Saccharomyces*, and the molds *Aspergillus*, *Fusarium*, and *Penicillium*, the microorganisms were more susceptible to irradiation when the moisture content was 22% vs. 15%.[10] As seen with bacteria, the degree of susceptibility differed between organisms, with the aspergilli and penicilli being more susceptible to irradiation at 10 Gy (0.01 kGy) than the others. The yeasts and the *Fusarium* mold species were the most resistant, being eliminated only upon irradiation at 120 Gy (0.12 kGy).

Effect of Irradiation on Microbial Toxins and Parasites

Toxins are chemical compounds, usually made of protein, which can affect the intestinal tract (*S. aureus* toxins), the nervous system (*C. botulinum* toxins), or other part of the human body upon ingestion. Given that toxins are simply molecules, the only effect that irradiation could have on them is that of breaking chemical bonds within the toxin structure, thereby inactivating it. However, since only 6 bonds per 10 million are cleaved due to irradiation, one might expect that toxins are fairly resistant to this process. In fact, this is what occurs, with doses as large as 8.0 kGy needed to inactivate microbial toxins in a buffer solution. Scientists have found that the medium in which the toxins are found can have a profound impact on their sensitivity to irradiation.[37] Toxins formed in beef slurry maintained 15% of their activity even after irradiation at 23.7 kGy, with increasing concentration of beef in the slurry affording increasing protection to the toxin against the effects of irradiation. Apparently, the components of such a slurry acted as quenchers of the radicals formed by irradiation, leaving fewer ions to react with the toxins.

Resistance to the effects of irradiation by toxins is also seen when the toxins are exposed to heating. The approach of microbiologists and health officials has therefore been one of prevention: to eliminate or inhibit the microorganisms responsible before toxin production can occur, which is easily done by both heating and irradiation. Even when irradiation is applied to products at doses not high enough to destroy all toxin-producing cells, these cells are not able to compete with the natural microbial flora of the product. The result is that the product spoils well before the toxin-producing cells are able to manufacture the chemicals. This has been found to be the case when chicken skins, inoculated with *Clostridium botulinum* type E cells, are irradiated at 3.0 kGy. Upon storage at 10°C (50°F), the normal flora of microorganisms causes the product to spoil after 8 days, with no toxin produced until the 14th day.[11]

Reduction or elimination of parasites by irradiation can be achieved by using doses that will simply sterilize these pests, rendering them unable to reproduce, or by killing the cysts, eggs, or larvae produced by these organisms. The basic mechanism is as explained for elimination of bacteria, yeasts, and molds, where irradiation breaks bonds in the DNA of these cells, making it impossible for normal replication to take place. Parasites like *Entamoeba histolytica* require a dose of at least 0.6 kGy for inhibition of growth, with 0.25 kGy achieving destruction of all viable cysts.[6] *Toxoplasma gondii* can only tolerate up to 0.1 kGy, at which dose the ability to infect tissue by the parasite is lost. A dose of 0.3 kGy is required to kill this organism.[6] In the case of the roundworm *Trichinella spiralis*, sterilization of adult forms is achieved at doses of 0.3 kGy, which also kills larvae and inhibits muscle invasion by the adult form.[6]

Effect of Irradiation on Microbial Quality of Various Food Products

RED MEAT AND POULTRY

Approval for irradiation of fresh meats has been given in the United States for poultry at levels between 1.5 and 3.0 kGy,[52] and for pork at levels between 0.30 and 1.0 kGy,[53] with no approval given for irradiation of beef as of this writing. Each of these approvals is based on specific goals: to eliminate *Salmonella* and similar pathogens from poultry, and to eliminate *Trichinella* from pork. The approvals were granted after numerous studies showed the efficacy of irradiation in achieving these goals. As part of these studies, D values have been determined for several pathogens of importance in poultry and red meat (Table 2.2).

As can be seen, irradiation at 1.5 to 3.0 kGy should result in elimination of at least 3 log cycles of even the most resistant pathogen on

Table 2.2. Survival of various food-borne bacterial pathogens exposed to irradiation in fresh meats

Organism	D value (in kGy)
Salmonella	0.40–0.50
Campylobacter	0.14–0.32
Listeria	0.40–0.60
Yersinia	0.04–0.21
Aeromonas	0.14–0.19
E. coli O157:H7	0.25–0.35

Source: Adapted from Radomyski et al.[36]

the list. The remaining question is, what will it do to the shelf life of these products? In one study, irradiation of chicken carcasses at 2.5 kGy resulted in a two-fold shelf life extension at 4°C (39.2°F), from 6 days in unirradiated chicken to 15 days in irradiated samples.[54] Irradiation at twice the dose, 5.0 kGy, extended the shelf life of fresh eviscerated poultry stored at 5°C (41°F) by 14 days.[24]

In examining the effect of irradiation on the number of microorganisms found in the normal flora of chicken, aerobic mesophilic counts on chicken wings were reduced from 10,000 to 44 cells per cm^2 after irradiation at 1.4 kGy.[46] Irradiation at 2.0 kGy reduced the microbial load in broiler chickens from 10,000 to 100 cells per chicken.[42] In studies involving chicken thighs, the total aerobic plate count was immediately reduced by 2 to 3 log cycles after irradiation at 1.0 kGy.[20] Moreover, the counts after 8 days of storage at 4°C (39.2°F) were lower in the irradiated thighs than in chicken thighs not irradiated and stored for only 2 days. In a similar study, chicken thighs irradiated at 2.5 kGy and stored at 0.5°C (32.9°F) showed no survivors at day 30, at a time when control thighs showed a contamination level of 6.1 log cycles.[19] Even after temperature abuse of chicken skins irradiated at 3.0 kGy and stored at 10°C (50°F), spoilage occurred at about 10 days in irradiated samples, compared with 5 days in controls.[11]

Irradiation of pork at the levels applied to chicken has also proven to be very effective in extending the shelf life of those products. Pork loins irradiated at 3.0 kGy in vacuum and stored at 2 to 4°C (35.6 to 39.2°F) took 90 days to spoil, compared with nonirradiated loins, which took 41 days.[29] Irradiation at lower levels (0.2 to 0.6 kGy) eliminated both the beef and pork tapeworms, *Taenia solium* and *Taenia saginata*, as well as the parasite *Trichinella spiralis* infecting pork tissue.[55]

SEAFOOD

Interest in irradiation of seafood has been sparked by concerns over the state of the inspection system of these products. As is the case with poultry and other meats, irradiation of seafood has been shown to be effective in eliminating pathogens of importance, such as *Vibrio parahaemolyticus* and *Aeromonas hydrophila* at medium doses. Table 2.3 shows the D values for several pathogenic organisms in fresh prawns. These D values vary in other seafood products.

Irradiation at the doses approved for poultry (1.5 to 3.0 kGy) would definitely prove to be effective in eliminating at least 3 log cycles of the most resistant organism in the above list from seafood. For frog legs, a similar product, irradiation at doses between 0.5 and 1.0 kGy completely eliminates *Vibrio cholerae*.[38] In extending the shelf life of seafood, irradiation at 1.3 kGy extended the life of fresh red hake by 6 to 13 days during storage at 3.3°C (38°F), and of cod fillets by 9 days when packed in ice.[30] Catfish irradiated at 0.5 to 1.0 kGy had its shelf life extended from 5 to 7 days to 20 to 30 days.[35]

One consideration in irradiation of seafood is the fat content of the product in question. Since irradiation forms radicals in fats, which tend to affect the organoleptic quality of the product, fish having very little fat can be irradiated at higher doses than fish containing higher fat levels. In this way, the shelf life of "low-fat" fish can be extended significantly more than that of regular fish. Flounder, crab meat, and oysters (all low-fat seafood) can be irradiated at 5.0 kGy without appreciable loss in quality. These products have a shelf life at 2°C (35.6°F) of 3 to 4 days prior to irradiation, which increases to 24 days (flounder), 50 days (crab meat), or 60 days (oysters) after irradiation at 5.0 kGy.[16] Table 2.4 presents the doses required to extend the shelf life of various seafood products.

Table 2.3. **Survival of various bacterial pathogens in fresh prawns**

Organism	D value (in kGy)
Vibrio spp.	0.11
Staphylococcus	0.29
E. coli	0.39
Salmonella spp.	0.48

Source: Adapted from Radomyski et al.[36]

Table 2.4.   Dose required to extend shelf life of fish and shellfish

Product	Optimal Dose (kGy)[a]	Shelf life at 0.5°C (33°F) (weeks)
Oysters	2.0	3–4
Shrimp	1.5	4
Sole fillets	2.0	2–3
Halibut steaks	2.0	2
Cooked crab meat	2.0	4–6
Haddock fillets	2.0	3–4
Cod fillets	1.5	4–5
Mackerel fillets	2.5	4–5

Source: Adapted from CAST.[6]

[a]Maximum dose applicable to frozen product packaged in air without detectable quality changes.

MILK AND DAIRY PRODUCTS

Irradiation of milk and dairy products has not been pursued to a great extent due to the effectiveness of heat pasteurization in eliminating pathogens of concern in those products. However, there is a need for irradiation of products which can become contaminated after milk is pasteurized, such as cheese and ice cream. The pathogen of concern in such products is *Listeria monocytogenes*, which is responsible for outbreaks involving cheese where several deaths occurred. The effective dose for a 12D process, to reduce this pathogen by 12 log cycles, has been calculated to be 16.8 kGy in cheese and 24.4 kG in ice cream.[17] This is based on D values for *L. monocytogenes* of 1.4 kGy in mozzarella cheese and 2.0 kGy in ice cream.

Irradiation at lower doses is effective and useful in eliminating molds from cheese. *Penicillium cyclopium* spores have a D value of 0.42 kGy in cheddar cheese, while *Aspergillus ochraceous* spores have a D value of 0.21 kGy in the same product. Irradiation of cheese at 0.5 kGy extended the shelf life by 5.5 days on samples containing *Penicillium*, while samples containing *Aspergillus* had a shelf life extension of 52.2 days.[3]

EGGS

Contamination of eggs by the pathogen *Salmonella enteritidis* has resulted in an increased number of outbreaks of food-borne illness in re-cent years, especially in the northeast part of the United States. Con-sumption of eggs has been regulated to the point that restaurants in some states are not allowed to serve this product unless it is thoroughly cooked. Most recently, an outbreak in 1994 due to consumption of ice cream contaminated with *S. enteritidis* has prompted health officials to suspect the involvement of raw eggs in the contamination of this prod-uct. In a study conducted in Yugoslavia, it was reported that the popu-lation of this organism would be reduced 1,000-fold by irradiation at 2.4 kGy in egg powder.[32] In investigating the effect of irradiation on several isolates of *S. enteritidis*, we have determined D values ranging from 0.25 to 0.50 kGy in whole eggs irradiated by x-rays. Thus, irradiation at 2.0 kGy would reduce the number of organisms by at least 4 $\log_{10}$ in this product.[43]

GRAINS AND SPICES

Disinfestation of grains by irradiation has been used to eliminate insects, as well as microbial pathogens. The action of ionizing radiation on insects is by physiological disturbances such as respiration, and by biological disturbances, such as alteration of enzymatic activity and DNA replication. When insect eggs are irradiated, they develop into lar-vae but fail to develop further. When the larvae are irradiated, the in-sects produced from these larvae are unable to reproduce.[6] The lethal dose (LD_{50}), the dose that kills 50% of the insect population, has been determined for several insect species. Mites have an LD_{50} of 3.0 kGy, while beetles require 2.0 kGy, and other granary pests require 0.7 kGy. An insect irradiated with a sublethal dose will not die, but may lose its ability to reproduce; this is known as the "sterilizing dose". The steril-ization dose for most insects is between 0.05 and 0.15 kGy, and between 0.60 and 0.80 kGy for mites.[50] Depending on the dose used (lethal vs. sublethal), either rapid and complete elimination of all insects in the grain will result, or reproduction of those insects will simply be inhib-ited. Which dose to use depends on the cost allowances, since the for-mer effect will require a higher dose, and presumably will cost more, than the latter. However, it must be remembered that any remaining in-sects in grains irradiated at sublethal levels will continue to consume the food product, even if they are unable to reproduce. Still, losses are less for grain irradiated at sublethal doses than for grain not irradiated at all.

Disinfestation of spices has been carried out mostly by fumigation with ethylene oxide and similar gases. Due to the highly toxic nature of this gas, an alternative is needed. The industry has been looking at irradiation with renewed interest, since this process can render spices free of insects and microbial pathogens. Irradiation has been approved in the United States to disinfect dry or dehydrated spices and seasonings at levels not to exceed 30 kGy.[15] Irradiation of black pepper, red chili, and turmeric, three of the most widely used spices, at 10 kGy can reduce the total microbial load to below 100 organism per gram, with complete elimination of *Bacillus cereus* spores.[45] Irradiation of spices at this dose was shown to eliminate 10^5 to 10^7 bacterial spores per gram, retaining sterility during 6 months of storage at room temperature. Complete destruction of 10^6 mold spores was attained with only 5.0 kGy. Comparison studies between irradiation at 6.5 kGy and ethylene oxide treatment showed irradiation to be more effective in reducing microbial counts below permissible levels in Spanish paprika, pointing to the benefits of this technology.[31]

FRUITS AND VEGETABLES

Fruits are currently treated to extend shelf life and to delay ripening by dipping in sulfur dioxide and similar chemicals. This is not a desirable practice, since consumers are increasingly desiring fresh produce that has been "organically" grown (without pesticides) and is without chemical residues. Irradiation has been approved in the United States at doses up to 1.0 kGy to inhibit maturation of fresh fruit and vegetables.[14] Doses of 10 kGy have been reported as being necessary to destroy all the various types of microorganisms usually present on the surface of fruit. However, such a high dose causes softening of the tissue, as well as deterioration of taste, precluding its use. Studies carried out over many years with fruits and berries reveal that irradiation doses of 2.5 to 3.0 kGy achieve maximum reduction in the number of contaminants without affecting quality.[6]

Sprouting is a major contributor to economic losses in long-stored vegetables. Most vegetables can be stored at 0°C (32°F) to suppress microbiological activity as well as sprouting. Some, like potatoes, are adversely affected by such storage and require other treatments to ensure a long shelf life. Potato tubers irradiated at 0.1 kGy do not sprout, even after being planted in soil. Even at doses as low as 0.03 kGy, sprouting of potatoes is significantly delayed.[48] We must note that vegetables differ in their radiation sensitivity. Onions require a dose of 0.05 to 0.06 kGy to delay sprouting, while garlic bulbs require 0.10 to 0.12 kGy.[49] Interestingly, onions are more sensitive to radiation during the first few weeks after harvest, while potatoes can be irradiated at any time just before sprouting to elicit an inhibitory effect. Similarly, germination in peanuts is greatly inhibited by irradiation. Peanuts irradiated at 5.0 to 20 kGy and stored at room temperature lost all germination capabilities, and mold was completely eliminated, even after 1 year.[8] Table 2.5 shows the minimum and maximum doses that should be applied to various vegetable commodities.

One important fact in irradiation of fruits and vegetables is that soon after being irradiated, these products become sensitive to the action of microorganisms that can come in contact with the surface after processing. Disease resistance is somehow weakened by irradiation, but it is restored with time. This occurs because tubers lose their capacity to form periderm around any mechanical damage the tuber may have suf-

Table 2.5. **Doses required to disinfest and to extend shelf life of fresh fruits and vegetables**

Commodity	Minimum Dose (kGy)	Maximum Dose (kGy)
Potatoes, onions, beets, radishes, turnips, yams	0.05–0.10	0.15
Asparagus	0.05–0.10	0.25
Mushrooms	0.06–0.50	1.0
Broccoli, cabbage, cauliflower, lettuce, spinach	0.15–0.30	0.30
Cucumber, eggplant, okra, peas, bell peppers, summer squash	0.15–0.30	0.50
Cantaloupe, melons, tomatoes	0.15–0.30	1.0
Apples, apricots, cherries, figs, peaches, pears, plums, berries	0.15–0.30	0.5–1.75
Avocado, grapefruit, grapes, kiwi, lemons, limes, olives, oranges, tangerines	0.15–0.30	0.25–0.75
Bananas, mangoes, papayas, pineapples, guava	0.15–0.30	1.0

Source: Adapted from CAST.[6]

fered during harvesting. In the absence of wound periderm, parasites may penetrate into the tuber and cause infection even after irradiation. For this reason, potatoes should not be irradiated immediately after harvest, to allow for formation of wound periderm in mechanically damaged parts before irradiation. It has been established that a reasonable time to wait between harvest and irradiation is 2 weeks, with the potatoes being kept at 15 to 20°C (59 to 68°F) at a relative humidity of 85%.[6] This lowering of disease resistance also occurs in fruits, but only after irradiation at doses higher than 1.0 kGy, which is the maximum limit approved for fruit irradiation in the United States.

Combination of Irradiation with Other Processes

Irradiation, as explained in this book, is a cold process: one that does not generate any appreciable heat in the product being irradiated. For this reason, food remains fresh-looking, with minimal changes to its organoleptic quality. However, for changes to be minimal, irradiation can be applied at low doses, but this diminishes its effectiveness in combating food-borne pathogens. There has been some interest in utilizing irradiation, in combination with other preservation methods, in order to reduce the number of microorganisms in foods while not affecting the quality of the product. In this section, we will discuss the use of various methods of preservation, in combination with food irradiation, to render foods safe and extend shelf life.

HEATING

Heat is the most widely used method of food preservation. It is effective in reducing or eliminating microbial contaminants, making products safe, and extending their shelf life. The only problem with heat is that it can have a significant effect on food quality. This effect is based on the ability of heat to coagulate proteins, inactivate enzymes, and destroy nutrients, all of which can alter the texture, flavor, and odor of a product. In one study, chicken breast was either heated in a Sous-vide process to achieve an internal temperature of 65.6°C (150°F), or heated and then irradiated at 2.9 kGy. *Listeria monocytogenes* counts in Sous-vide-treated chicken reached 10^7 cells per gram after 8 weeks of storage at 2°C (35.6°F), while no cells were detected in chicken exposed to both heating and irradiation.[44] Thermoradiation (the use of heat + irradiation) also resulted in greater reduction of the number of *Salmonella enteritidis* cells in egg white, compared with heat or irradiation alone.[40] This was also the case in inactivation of foot-and-mouth disease virus in beef heated at 78°C (172.4°F) for 20 minutes followed by irradiation at 15 to 25 kGy.[28] Also, heating at 60°C (140°F) for 30 minutes followed by irradiation at 4.0 kGy inhibited aflatoxin production in maize meal broth, compared with only irradiation at this dose.

A study was conducted to examine whether it is more effective to heat before irradiation than the other way around. Irradiation prior to heating was more effective in decreasing the total number of microbial contaminants from chicken than heating followed by irradiation. Irradiation at 0.90 kGy followed by heating at 60°C (140°F) for 3 minutes, decreased the number of microorganisms by 8.9 log cycles, compared with the other way around, which decreased the number of cells by 6.4 log cycles.[47]

MODIFIED ATMOSPHERES

Modified Atmosphere Packaging (MAP) of foods is one of the most used food preservation technologies. The quality of such foods is superior to that of thermally processed products, and their shelf stability has allowed the United States to better compete in foreign markets. The combined effect of irradiation with this packaging method has been extensively studied, and its benefits are self-evident. One can expect foods packaged in this way to be of higher quality than those packaged in an atmosphere where oxygen predominates. However, survival of microorganisms in such products is not as predictable as one may imagine. For instance, while meat packaged in air showed more survivors than that packaged in vacuum or in CO_2,[18] irradiation of lactobacilli in meat after packaging in N_2 resulted in the highest number of survivors of all packaging gases tested. However, irradiation at 1.0 kGy of cod fillets packaged in 60% CO_2/40% air extended the shelf life of the product to 25 days, while fillets packaged in air spoiled after 14 days in ice.[30] It is possible that oxygen is used up by the normal microbial flora of some products, resulting in its unavailability for radical formation. This un-availability can result in shelf life extension of products that initially contained oxygen. At any rate, use of CO_2 does have an antimicrobial effect in and of itself and is recommended for reducing the number of microbial pathogens and for extending the shelf life of foods.

There have been some concerns over the use of vacuum packaging in medium-dose irradiation of foods that could contain spores of the pathogen *Clostridium botulinum*. It is postulated that such anoxic con-ditions may favor germination, growth, and toxin production by this or-ganism, known as one of the most dangerous anaerobes of the microbial world. Contrary to popular belief, toxin production by this organism is actually faster in pork packaged under 20% oxygen compared with samples packaged under anoxic atmospheres, such as in 100% N_2 gas.[26] In addition, toxin production occurs faster in samples packaged in 15 to 30% CO_2, but it is delayed in 45 to 75% CO_2.[27] In both cases, irradia-tion at 1.0 kGy has delayed toxin production, regardless of the gas. Fi-nally, it has been shown that, even though irradiation at medium doses under vacuum kills pathogens, it does not destroy all the spoilage mi-croorganisms. These are able to grow rapidly after irradiation, outcom-peting *Clostridium botulinum* for nutrients, thus spoiling the product well before toxin can be produced.[11]

Fruits and vegetables are living organisms from the point of har-vest through shipping, undergoing respiration, maturation, and ripening while they are being transported to their destination. In a product pack-aged under a modified atmosphere, these processes are affected by the existing gases and by the rate at which they are permeated through the package. The levels of CO_2 and O_2 will shift and change according to CO_2 production and O_2 consumption by the product itself and as they relate to the amount of CO_2 added to the package as part of MAP.[4] Di-rect gas injection of strawberries to raise CO_2 levels delays ripening while also inhibiting the growth of organisms that spoil the product, such as *Rhizopus nigricans*. Irradiation at doses between 0.25 and 0.35 kGy have typically been used to inhibit or delay ripening of many fruits.[6] Some fruits, such as bananas and strawberries, are not refriger-ated due to chilling injury that can result at temperatures below 10°C (50°F). Modified Atmosphere Packaging can be used in conjunction with irradiation to further extend shelf life without the need for low-temperature storage of these products.

OTHER

Phosphates have been used by the food industry, both to inhibit microorganisms, and to enhance the water-binding of certain meat products. In one study, sodium acid pyrophosphate at a level of 0.4% in ground pork added 2 days to the shelf life of the product. Irradiation at 1.0 kGy added an extra 2 days, for a total of 10 days of shelf life, compared with 6 days for controls.[12] Salt has also been used in conjunction with irradiation and has been found to be effective in controlling microbial growth. However, the type of salt used can make a difference, with 2.5% sodium chloride (NaCl) in combination with 10 kGy being more effective than potassium chloride (KCl) or magnesium chloride (MgCl$_2$) at inhibiting botulinum toxin production in frankfurters.[1]

High pressure is an emerging technology, proven effective against vegetative cells in many food products. This process, much like heating, changes the texture and flavor of foods, mainly through protein precipitation and tissue softening. We have effectively used it, in conjunction with irradiation, to increase the shelf life of whole chicken breast, and to reduce the number of vegetative cells and spores of *Clostridium sporogenes*. High pressure-treatment at 100,000 psi seems to be more effective prior to irradiation at 3.0 kGy than the other way around, primarily in reducing the spores, a phenomenon probably due to the physical disruption of the spore coat, which may sensitize the organism to irradiation.[9]

Final Comments

Irradiation, if used properly, can have substantial benefits for the food industry. Among the most significant are its ability to (1) increase food safety, (2) delay senescence of fruits and vegetables, (3) increase the shelf life of perishable products, and (4) reduce the chance for post-processing contamination.

Food safety is increased by virtue of destruction of microbial pathogens, many of which can be eliminated totally from fresh products by irradiation at 1.5 kGy. Delay of senescence of produce is achieved at relatively low doses, below 1.0 kGy, but irradiation needs to be applied at a specific time in order to minimize losses due to susceptibility to microbial attack during storage. Increasing shelf life is one of the most significant effects of irradiation, opening up export markets that were previously unreachable. Such delay of spoilage will prove to be the ruler by which some consumers judge the usefulness of this process, and whether it is worth paying for. Finally, because products are irradiated after packaging, this technology ensures that the food is delivered in as clean a fashion as possible, since the problems of postprocessing contamination in the plant are eliminated.

The Hazard Analysis Critical Control Points (HACCP) system is a system that provides a rational approach to solving the problem of contamination of foods by pathogenic organisms.[34] Within HACCP, determination of critical control points (CCPs) during the preparation or processing of a product is one of the most significant steps required to prevent or control hazards inherent in the product. It would be easy to imagine the introduction of irradiation as the last CCP in the processing of ground beef patties after packaging and before shipping to the retail operation. In fact, with this technology in place, outbreaks due to undercooking would be significantly minimized, since pathogens that would cause food-borne illness would not be present in the product. Monitoring of this CCP would simply entail verification of the irradiation process by the record-keeping now required of all irradiation facilities.

Irradiation, however, should not be used to make "dirty" products (those heavily contaminated with microorganisms) clean again. To attempt to do so would require doses much higher than those needed to eliminate normal background levels. This would result in significant damage to the quality of the product, and in high costs to the processor in terms of energy. It is not logical to think that food irradiation will be used in this manner, anymore than heat processing is used in that way. Therefore, adherence to Good Manufacturing Practices (GMPs) would still be the rule, just as with any other process. In addition, proper refrigeration would be carried out for products irradiated at low to medium doses, since these levels do not sterilize the food. Irradiation, in common with most other processes, is not an all-encompassing solution to the problem of microbial contamination. It is simply one of several solutions, which, together with GMPs and HACCP, will work to make foods safe.

References

1. Barbut, S., A.J. Maurer, and D.W. Thayer. 1987. Gamma-irradiation of *Clostridium botulinum* inoculated turkey frankfurters formulated with different chloride salts and polyphosphates. J. Food Sci. 52:1137-1139.

2. Berkelman, R.L., R.T. Bryan, M.T. Osterholm, J.W. LeDuc, and J.M. Hughes. 1994. Infectious disease surveillance: a crumbling foundation. Science 264:368-370.

3. Blank, G., K. Shamsuzzaman, and S. Sohal. 1992. Use of electron beam irradiation for mold decontamination on cheddar cheese. J. Dairy Sci. 75:13-18.

4. Brody, A.L. 1989. Controlled/Modified Atmosphere/Vacuum Packaging of Foods. Food & Nutrition Press, Inc., Trumbull, Connecticut.

5. CAST. 1994. Foodborne pathogens: risks and consequences. Report No. 122. Council for Agricultural Science and Technology, Ames, Iowa.

6. CAST. 1989. Ionizing energy in food processing and pest control: II. Applications. Report No. 115. Council for Agricultural Science and Technology, Ames, Iowa.

7. CAST. 1986. Ionizing energy in food processing and pest control: I. Wholesomeness of food treated with ionizing energy. Report No. 109. Council for Agricultural Science and Technology, Ames, Iowa.

8. Chiou, R.Y., S.L. Shyu, and C.C. Tsai. 1991. Characterization of gamma irradiated peanut kernels stored one year under ambient and frozen conditions. J. Food Sci. 56:1375-1377.

9. Crawford, Y.E., E.A. Murano, and D.G. Olson. 1994. Effect of hydrostatic pressure in combination with heat and/or irradiation on the survival of *Clostridium sporogenes* in chicken. Abstr. Ann. Meet. Int. Assoc. Milk Food Environ. Sanit., San Antonio, Texas.

10. Cuero, R.G., J.E. Smith, and J. Lacey. 1986. The influence of gamma irradiation and sodium hypochlorite sterilization on maize seed microflora and germination. Food Microbiol. 3:107-113.

11. Dezfulian, M., and J.G. Bartlett. 1987. Effects of irradiation on growth and toxigenicity of *Clostridium botulinum* types A and B inoculated onto chicken skins. Appl. Environ. Microbiol. 53:201-203.

12. Ehioba, R.M., A.A. Kraft, R.A. Molins, H.W. Walker, D.G. Olson, G.

Subbaraman, and R.P. Skowronski. 1987. Effect of low-dose (100 krad) gamma radiation on the microflora of vacuum-packaged ground pork with and without added sodium phosphates. J. Food Sci. 52:1477-1480, 1505.

13. El-Zawahry, Y.A. and D.B. Rowley. 1979. Radiation resistance and injury of *Yersinia enterocolitica*. Appl. Environ. Microbiol. 37:50-54.

14. FDA. 1986. Irradiation in the production, processing, and handling of food. Final Rule. Federal Register. 51:13375-13399.

15. FDA. 1984. Irradiation in the production, processing, and handling of food. Federal Register. 49:5714-5722.

16. Grodner, R.M. and L.S. Andrews. 1991. Irradiation. In: Microbiology of Marine Food Products, pp. 429-440. D.R. Ward and C.R. Hackney, eds. Van Nostrand Rinehold, New York, New York.

17. Hashisaka, A.E., S.D. Weagant, and F.M. Dong. 1989. Survival of *Listeria monocytogenes* in mozzarella cheese and ice cream exposed to gamma irradiation. J. Food Prot. 52:490-492.

18. Hastings, J.W., W.H. Holzapfel, and J.G. Niemand. 1986. Radiation resistance of lactobacilli isolated from radurized meat relative to growth and environment. Appl. Environ. Microbiol. 52:898-901.

19. Heath, J.L. and S.L. Owens. 1992. Electron beam irradiation: effect of surface dose variation on analytical values and shelf life of chicken. J. Musc. Foods 3:191-202.

20. Heath, J.L., S.L. Owens, and S. Tesch. 1990. Effects of high-energy electron irradiation of chicken meat on *Salmonella* and aerobic plate count. Poult. Sci. 69:150-156.

21. Hiemstra, H., M. Tersmette, A.H. Vos, J. Over, M.P. VanBerkel, and H. deBree. 1991. Inactivation of human immunodeficiency virus by gamma irradiation and its effect on plasma and coagulation factors. Transf. 31:32-39.

22. Huhtanen, C.N., R.K. Jenkins, and D.W. Thayer. 1989. Gamma radiation sensitivity of *Listeria monocytogenes*. J. Food Prot. 52:610-613.

23. ICGFI. 1991. Facts about food irradiation. Int. Atom. Ener. Agen., Vienna, Austria.

24. Idziak, E.S. and K. Incze. 1968. Radiation treatment of foods. I. Radurization of fresh eviscerated poultry. Appl. Microbiol. 16:1061-1066.

25. Lambert, A.D. and R.B. Maxcy. 1984. Effect of gamma radiation on *Campylobacter jejuni*. J. Food Sci. 49:665-667, 674.

26. Lambert, A.D., J.P. Smith, and K.L. Dodds. 1991a. Effect of initial O_2 and CO_2 and low-dose irradiation on toxin production by *Clostridium botulinum* in MAP fresh pork. J. Food Prot. 54:939-944.

27. Lambert, A.D., J.P. Smith, and K.L. Dodds. 1991b. Effect of headspace CO_2 concentration on toxin production by *Clostridium botulinum* in MAP, irradiated fresh pork. J. Food Prot. 54:588-592.

28. Lasta, J., J.H. Blackwell, A. Sadir, M. Gallanger, F. Marcoveccio, M. Zamorano, B. Ludder, and R. Rodriguez. 1992. Combined treatments of heat,

irradiation, and pH effects on infectivity of foot-and-mouth disease virus in bovine tissues. J. Food Sci. 57:36-39.

29. Lebepe, S., R.A. Molins, S.P. Chawen, H. Farrar IV, and R.P. Skowronski. 1990. Changes in microflora and other characteristics of vacuum-packaged pork loins irradiated at 3.0 kGy. J. Food Sci. 55:918-924.

30. Licciardello, J.J., E.M. Rakesi, B.E. Tuhkunen, and L.D. Racicot. 1984. Effect of some potentially synergistic treatments in combination with 100 krad irradiation on the iced shelf life of cod fillets. J. Food Sci. 49:1341-1346, 1375.

31. Llorente Franco, S., J.L. Gimenez, F. Martinez Sanchez, and F. Romojaro. 1986. Effectiveness of ethylene oxide and gamma irradiation on the microbiological population of three types of paprika. J. Food Sci. 51:1571-1572, 1574.

32. Matic, S., V. Minokovic, B. Katusin-Razem, and D. Razem. 1990. The eradication of *Salmonella* in egg powder by gamma irradiation. J. Food Prot. 53:111-114.

33. Patterson, M. 1988. Sensitivity of bacteria to irradiation on poultry meat under various atmospheres. Lett. Appl. Microbiol. 7:55-58.

34. Pierson, M.D. and D.A. Corlett. 1992. HACCP: Principles and Applications. Van Nostrand Rinehold, New York, New York.

35. Przybylski, L.A., M.W. Finerty, R.M. Grodner, and D.L. Gerdes. 1989. Extension of shelf life of iced fresh channel catfish fillets using modified atmospheric packaging and low dose irradiation. J. Food Sci. 54:269-273.

36. Radomyski, T., E.A. Murano, D.G. Olson, and P.S. Murano. 1994. Elimination of pathogens of significance in food by low-dose irradiation: a review. J. Food Prot. 57:73-86.

37. Rose, S.A., N.K. Modi, H.S. Tranter, N.E. Bailey, M.F. Stringer, and P. Hambleton. 1988. Studies on the irradiation of toxins of *Clostridium botulinum* and *Staphylococcus aureus*. J. Appl. Bact. 65:223-229.

38. Sang, F.C., M.E. Hugh-Jones, and H.V. Hagstad. 1987. Viability of *Vibrio cholerae* O:1 on frog legs under frozen and refrigerated conditions and low dose radiation treatment. J. Food Prot. 50:662-664.

39. Satin, M. 1993. Food Irradiation: A Guidebook. Technomic Publishing, Lancaster, Pennsylvania.

40. Schaffner, D.F., M.K. Hamdy, R.T. Toledo, and M.L. Tift. 1989. Salmonella inactivation in liquid whole egg by thermoradiation. J. Food Sci. 54:902-905.

41. Seiler, D.A.L. 1978. The microbiology of cake and its ingredients. Food Trade Rev. 32:339.

42. Sekhar, R.K., D.R. Rao, G.R. Sunki, and C.B. Chawan. 1991. Effect of gamma irradiation of whole chicken carcasses on bacterial loads and fatty acids. J. Food Sci. 56:371-372.

43. Serrano, L. and E.A. Murano. 1994. Effect of irradiation on survival

of *Salmonella enteritidis* in whole eggs and liquid whole eggs. Abst. Ann. Meet. Int. Assoc. Milk Food Environ. Sanit., San Antonio, Texas.

44. Shamsuzzaman, K., N. Chuaqui-Offermanns, L. Lucht, T. McDougall, and J. Borsa. 1992. Microbiological and other characteristics of chicken breast meat following electron beam and sous-vide treatments. J. Food Prot. 55:528-533.

45. Sharma, A., S.R. Padwal-Desai, and P.M. Nair. 1989. Assessment of microbiological quality of some gamma irradiated indian spices. J. Food Sci. 54:489-490.

46. Thayer, D.W., C.Y. Dickerson, D.R. Rao, G. Boyd, and C.B. Chawan. 1992. Destruction of *Salmonella typhimurium* on chicken wings by gamma irradiation. J. Food Sci. 57:586-589.

47. Thayer, D.W., S. Songprasertchai, and G. Boyd. 1991. Effects of heat and ionizing radiation on *Salmonella typhimurium* in mechanically deboned chicken meat. J. Food Prot. 54:718-724.

48. Thomas, P. 1984a. Radiation preservation of foods of plant origin. Part I. Potatoes and other tuber crops. CRC Crit. Rev. Food Sci. Nutr. 19:327-370.

49. Thomas, P. 1984a. Radiation preservation of foods of plant origin. Part II. Onions and other bulb crops. CRC Crit. Rev. Food Sci. Nutr. 21:95-136.

50. Tilton, E.W. and A.K. Burditt. 1983. Insect disinfestation of grain and fruit. In: Preservation of Food by Ionizing Radiation. Vol. III, pp. 215-229. E.S. Josephson and M.S. Patterson, eds. CRC Press, Boca Raton, Florida.

51. Todd, E.C.D. 1989. Preliminary estimates of costs of foodborne disease in the United States. J. Food Prot. 52:595-601.

52. USDA. 1990. Irradiated food production, processing, and handling-ionizing radiation control of food-borne pathogens in poultry. Federal Register. 55:18538, 19701.

53 .USDA. 1985. Irradiation in the production, processing, and handling of food. Federal Register. 50:29658.

54. Varabioff, Y., G.E. Mitchell, and S.M. Nottingham. 1992. Effects of irradiation on bacterial load and *Listeria monocytogenes* in raw chicken. J. Food Prot. 55:389-391.

55. Verster, A., T.A. duPlessis, and L.W. van den Heever. 1977. The eradiacation of tapeworm in pork and beef carcasses by irradiation. Radiat. Phys. Chem. 9:769-773.

Suggested Readings

Banwart, G.J. 1989. Basic food microbiology. Van Nostrand Reinhold, New York, NY.
Brock, T.D., M.T. Madigan, J.M. Martinko, and J. Parker. 1994. Biology of microorganisms, 7th ed. Prentice Hall, Inc., Englewood Cliffs, NJ.

Cliver, D.O. Foodborne diseases. 1990. Academic Press, San Diego, CA.

Diehl, J.F. 1990. Safety of irradiated foods. Marcel Dekker, Inc., New York, NY.

Jay, J. 1992. Modern food microbiology, 4th ed. Van Nostrand Reinhold, New York, NY.

Josephson, E.S. and M.S. Peterson. 1983. Preservation of food by ionizing radiation. CRC Press, Inc., Boca Raton, FL.

Murray, D.R. 1990. Biology of food irradiation. John Wiley & Sons, Inc., New York, NY.

CHAPTER 3

QUALITY OF IRRADIATED FOODS

PETER S. MURANO, PhD

Introduction

The foods people consume can be of interest for various reasons, including economic, cultural, psychological, philosophical, and religious ones. However, the fact of the biological necessity of food is, from the standpoint of existence, the most critically important. Similarly, although the individual foods consumed may be notable for reasons of sensory appeal (appearance, flavor, texture, and aroma), it is their nutrient content which directly translates into the nourishment needed by the human body in order to survive and flourish.

Scientists have identified over 50 essential nutrients, that is, required nutrients that the body cannot make itself and must therefore be obtained from food sources. Coming from both plant and animal sources, the essential nutrients are constituents of the following food components: water, carbohydrate, protein, and fat (the major "macronutrients"); and vitamins and minerals (the major "micronutrients"). In order for the body to experience optimum growth and functioning, all of the essential nutrients must be provided in sufficient and balanced quantities.

The body requires food on a daily basis. Ideally this would require that fresh foods be gathered and supplied for immediate consumption. In today's world, this can be impractical or impossible to achieve. Be-

63

cause of this, and since fresh foods undergo rapid quality deterioration and spoilage and may only be available "in-season", methods of food processing and preservation have been developed.

The focus of food preservation is to maintain the freshness and nutrient quality of foods by preventing the spoilage caused by the microorganisms which contaminate food. Of equal importance is the need to control the deterioration of foods caused by enzyme and chemical reactions which may be naturally occurring in the food (endogenous reactions) or those undesirable changes due to the interactions of foods with substances in their immediate vicinity (exogenous reactions). This control is accomplished by manipulating various environmental parameters such as acidity, moisture, and temperature (Table 3.1).

Since the various processing techniques exert their influences differently, they offer varying degrees of effectiveness and may exhibit specific limitations of application. For example, heat sterilization is the most effective process in terms of eliminating spoilage microbes, but this is at the expense of some vitamin and protein degradation. Acidity inhibits the growth of spoilage microorganisms, and can be accomplished by the addition of acidulants or by the process of acidic fermentation. Loss of nutrients by these techniques is small, though acidification is not applicable to all food systems. Refrigeration and drying as a means of preservation have been practiced for years. Freezing essentially stops enzyme activity and associated food quality losses (enzymes act to break down nutrients in food into smaller products, which can cause undesirable color, texture, flavor, and aroma changes) while creating only minimal vitamin loss. Food irradiation as a process is the most recent form of food preservation.

Irradiation, or the use of ionizing energy, draws upon one of sev-

Table 3.1. Procedures used to achieve food preservation

Environmental Manipulation	Food-processing Technique
Acidity (pH decrease)	Fermentation; use of acidulants
Chemical control	Additive processing
Irradiation	Ionizing energy
Moisture decrease	Drying; dehydration
Temperature decrease	Refrigeration; freezing
Temperature increase	Blanching; cooking; microwaving; pasteurization; sterilization

eral possible energy forms in order to exert its effects: high frequency gamma rays (either cobalt or cesium), x-rays, or accelerated electrons. These energy forms are termed "ionizing" due to the effect they have on molecules: they create "ions", which are electrically charged positive and negative. The ions which form are reactive for a brief period before stabilizing and becoming deactivated. It is during the short span of this activity that irradiation causes effects which enable it to be regarded as a means of preserving foods. Regardless of the energy source, the targets of the process in the application to food preservation are the spoilage and pathogenic (those responsible for outbreaks of food poisoning) microorganisms and, to a lesser degree, the degradative enzymes.

Irradiation is termed a "cold process" as applied to food preservation, because it does not add heat to foods. As a result, the nutritional degradations caused by heating are not created. There is, though, some potential for nutrient loss (especially vitamins) and texture and flavor changes when high irradiation doses are applied to foods. For these reasons, the recommended dose level in applying this technology to food preservation is 10 kGy or less. When applied within this range, irradiation is highly effective in controlling food-borne spoilage organisms in foods. Also, the process inhibits the maturation, senescence, and sprouting of fresh fruits and vegetables, thus extending their shelf life. Irradiation of flour, cereals, and fruits and vegetables can replace the use of chemical fumigation for disinfestation (the killing of insect pests). It is important to remember that prior to consumption foods often must undergo some form of storage for varying periods of time; therefore proper packaging is a mandatory adjunct to food processing, be it by irradiation or some other method, in order to maintain food quality.

In this chapter, the emphasis is on the quality of food which has been irradiated. If irradiation as a process is to be regarded as useful and beneficial to modern society, then the quality of irradiated foods must not be in doubt. The objective of this chapter is to present the subject matter in as simple a fashion as possible so that all readers, including those with little scientific background, will be served. Information in this chapter is not meant to cover in detail the entire scope of topics related to the quality of irradiated foods. Those who are interested in more detail can utilize the suggested readings at the chapter's end. This chapter was written to be a concise overview, providing a basic introduction to the following topics: (1) the nutrients in foods and what happens to them when foods are irradiated; (2) methods to detect whether or not food has been irradiated, including the formation of radicals; and (3) the quality of irradiated foods, with focus on sensory quality.

The issue of the safety of foods *irradiated with 10 kGy* or less of ionizing energy has been addressed by leading scientists worldwide— the November 1980 joint FAO/WHO/IAEA Expert Committee on the Wholesomeness of Irradiated Food concluded that "the irradiation of any food commodity up to an overall average dose of 10 kGy causes no toxicological hazard and hence toxicological testing of foods so treated is no longer required."[18]

There is no need to devote space in this book to the issue of the *safety* of irradiated food, since the committee's conclusion was based upon its informed examination of a very large body of evidence from thorough, rigorous scientific investigations and inquiries spanning years of study. In the nearly one and one-half decades which have followed since its conclusion was made known, research carried out using the latest, most sensitive, and most advanced and critical experimental designs has substantiated that conclusion. Those interested in reading further on the topic of the safety of irradiated foods should consult the book on the subject by Diehl.[10]

Nutrients in Foods vs. Irradiation

The main focus of this section is to offer a general overview of the key nutrients found in foods and to identify the possible changes caused to those nutrients by the irradiation process. It must be realized that one of the goals of this book is to provide information in a manner which is comprehensible to those without a technical background. In an effort to achieve this objective, the discussions will include brief accounts of the major nutrient classes and food sources as well as a sampling of the most recent research findings regarding the effects of irradiation on each nutrient. For more detailed information and a more extensive discussion of research findings, a selection of review articles is provided at the end of the chapter.

WATER

Water is the most indispensable nutrient. The body can continue alive for weeks without food, but for only a few days without water. Foods contain varying amounts of water, with some solid foods containing more water on a percentage basis than do some beverages (Table 3.2).

Table 3.2. Percentage of water in some foods

Food	% Water
Iceberg lettuce	96
Apple	85
Dried apricots	32
Baked potato	75
Milk	90
Milkshake	73
Cooked eggs	70
Bread	35

Since most foods we consume are composed of much water, the ionization of water is the predominant reaction to occur upon irradiation of a food. Chemically, water (symbolized as H_2O) is composed of two hydrogen atoms joined to one oxygen atom. When water molecules are irradiated, they lose an electron, with production of a positively charged water radical resulting. Shown in Figure 3.1 are the additional reactions and products which can occur (formation of hydrated electrons, hydroxyl radicals, hydrogen ions, and hydrogen atoms).[7]

$$H_2O + \text{ionizing energy} \rightarrow (H_2O\bullet)^+ + e_{aq}^-$$

[water ionizes into water radical plus hydrated electron]

$$(H_2O\bullet)^+ \rightarrow OH\bullet + H^+$$

[water radical decomposes into hydroxyl radical and hydrogen ion]

$$H_2O \rightarrow (OH\bullet)^+ + H\bullet$$

[water disassociates into hydroxyl radical and hydrogen atom]

FIGURE 3.1. The radiolysis of water.

The free radicals which result from the ionization of water in a food can react with any of the food's other component nutrient molecules or additives/ingredients. The potential to form a great many different so-called "radiolytic products" is thus quite high, though the actual quantity formed is measurably extremely small.[35] Though these reactions occur with great rapidity (sometimes in fractions of a second), the radicals which result are detectable if they become trapped within hard portions of foods (extremely dry, frozen, or dense areas, such as in seeds, pits, or bone). Recognition of these entrapped radicals forms the basis of a means to detect whether or not a food has been irradiated (see Detection of Irradiated Foods in this chapter).

CARBOHYDRATES

Carbohydrates are molecules composed of sugar units, which contain particular arrangements of carbon, hydrogen, and oxygen atoms. The kinds of carbohydrates found in foods can be categorized according to their size. The smallest are the monosaccharides and disaccharides (simple sugars such as glucose and sucrose), with the larger complex carbohydrates (pectin, fiber, and starch) referred to as polysaccharides. The prefixes mono-, di- and poly- refer to the number of sugar units forming a particular carbohydrate molecule. An overview of carbohydrates and food sources is provided in Table 3.3.

Other sources of dietary carbohydrate are the manufactured by-products of food technology. These include the sugar alcohols mannitol

Table 3.3.   Carbohydrate types and food sources

Type	Food Source
Monosaccharide	
Glucose	Sweeteners, fruits
Fructose	Honey, fruits
Disaccharide	
Sucrose	Sweeteners (cane sugar) and fruits
Lactose	Milk, milk products
Maltose	Grains
Polysaccharides	
Starches	Grains, beans, potatoes
Fiber	Grains, beans, nuts, fruits, vegetables

and sorbitol, which are used as sugar substitutes; high fructose corn syrup, an alternative sweetener used especially in beverages; and poly-dextrose, a nondigestible texturizer and bulking agent used in low calorie foods.

Irradiation Effects.   The major effects of irradiation on the carbohydrates found in foods are basically the same as those caused by cooking and other types of processing treatments. These include shortening of large polysaccharide chains, the degradation of starch and cellulose into simple sugars, and the formation of sugar acids, ketones, and other sugars from monosaccharides. The fact that amino acids and proteins can protect carbohydrates from irradiation degradation must be considered when comparing results from experiments with model systems (carbohydrate isolates in water) and whole foods (containing a variety of nutrients, including carbohydrates).[37] Irradiation of solutions of carbohydrates in water, as with cooking, results in the breakdown of complex carbohydrate molecules into simpler compounds. Polysaccharides yield smaller units, such as dextrins, glucose, maltose, and other radiolytic products. Starches and cellulose, which are not easily digested by enzymes due to the way the long glucose chains are packed, are made more susceptible to enzymatic action (hydrolysis) by treatment with irradiation.

Irradiation of various fruits and vegetables to prevent storage spoilage has been carried out, and the effects on carbohydrates noted. For instance, irradiated dates (doses ranging to 10 kGy) were reported to produce typical carbohydrate hydrolysis products.[1] The irradiation (100 kGy) of hulless barley resulted in the breakage of starch into smaller units (of amylose and amylopectin), and in enhanced sensitivity to decomposition by the enzyme which digests starch, amylase.[6] Degradation of starch results in a decrease in one of its functional properties, that of forming a viscous paste when heated in solution. Studies on the viscosities of black and white peppers irradiated to 5 kGy showed decreased viscosities upon irradiation due to the effects on starch.[16] Brown rice samples irradiated at 1.0-3.0 kGy in order to alter starch to improve its uptake of water and lower cooking time showed increased starch damage without alterations in amylose content with increasing dose.

The viscosities of heated rice flour/water slurries decreased with increasing irradiation dose.[30]

From the standpoint of quality, one must be concerned with the digestibility and availability of the carbohydrates in an irradiated food for energy (the nutritional aspects) with the role those carbohydrates play in maintaining the food's typical color, odor, flavor, and texture (the nonnutritional quality aspects), and with the functional properties of the carbohydrates (e.g., swelling and thickening of flour due to starch gelatinization; structurizing and drying functions of sugars used in baking; sweetening power of sugars; crystallization of sugars). Both studies employing model systems and those focusing on intact carbohydrate-containing foods have indicated that at low dose levels (<1.0 to a few kGy) the nutritional consequences of irradiation were negligible, whereas nonnutritional quality changes have been observed and were related to the dose and storage time and conditions.[10] For instance, irradiation at high doses causes softening of fruits and vegetables due to its effects on plant cell walls and on the pectins which provide the structural rigidity to plant tissue.[6] The use of irradiation in connection with fruits and vegetables which are to be consumed "whole in the skin" is therefore limited, because of postirradiation quality effects that can result at doses above 1.0 kGy. An overview of the effects of irradiation on carbohydrates is presented in Table 3.4.

In summary, the effects of low to medium doses (<1.0 to 10 kGy) of irradiation have mild effects on carbohydrates which do not significantly alter either carbohydrate functionality in foods or their nutritional value.

Table 3.4.   Irradiation effects on carbohydrates

Carbohydrate Type	Nutritional Effect	Possible Quality and Functional Effect
Simple sugars	1	5, 6, 7
Disaccharides	1, 2	5
Polysaccharides	1, 2, 3	4, 5, 7, 8

KEY: 1 = production of other sugars or sugar breakdown products; 2 = production of simple sugars; 3 = production of glucose, maltose, dextrins; 4 = loss of jelling property (due to pectin degradation); 5 = browning reactions; 6 = reduced sweetness; 7 = reduced functionality in baking; 8 = reduced availabilty of fiber.

PROTEINS

The class of nutrients called proteins contain the same atoms of carbon, hydrogen, and oxygen as do the carbohydrates, but in addition they also contain nitrogen. Some may also contain the element sulfur. Proteins are composed of subunits called amino acids. There are 20 naturally occurring amino acids, all consisting of the same basic structure. What differences exist are due to the makeup of the side chain portions of amino acids. Amino acids are linked together by peptide bonds to form dipeptides (two amino acids in size), tripeptides (three amino acids in size) and polypeptides (four or more amino acids in size). Protein molecules are polypeptides which consist of many chains of amino acids and the peptide bonds which hold them together. Their three-dimensional shapes can resemble either parallel strands of amino acids linked by the various side chains (the "fibrous" proteins, such as collagen, elastin, and the muscle proteins actin and myosin) or twisted, irregular structures (the "globular" proteins, such as enzymes, albumin, and myoglobin).

Food protein sources can be animal in origin, for instance meats, poultry, fish, eggs, and dairy products, or plant-derived, specifically nuts, legumes, cereals, and grains. Fruits and vegetables are poor sources of protein, being mostly water and carbohydrate. Animal proteins are about ten times more concentrated per unit weight than plant proteins and also are of higher quality, in that all of the essential amino acids are present. Plants are very low or lacking in one or more of the following essential amino acids: lysine, methionine, and tryptophan.

Irradiation Effects. The irradiation of proteins at high doses is known to produce denaturation (unfolding of the protein structure), formation of protein radicals due to interactions with water molecule radicals, and a host of reactions to the constituent amino acid subunits (Table 3.5). Low doses of irradiation can cause a very minor breakdown of food proteins into smaller molecular weight fragments and amino acids, while very high doses (in the hundreds of kGy) can cause cleavage of the amino acid side chains.[36] The application of the small to medium dose range of ionizing energy has been heavily investigated in protein foods and in protein isolates, and it has been determined that such treatments cause no more protein degradation than does conventional steam heat sterilization.

As was the case in our discussion of the importance of studying the irradiation of carbohydrates, the irradiation of protein and protein-containing foods may be considered on three levels. First, determine the effect irradiation might have upon the availability of protein to the body (e.g., amino acid profile, biological value, percent digestibility) in order to perform its usual functions (nutritional effect). Second, determine what changes, if any, occur in the appearance, odor, flavor, and texture of irradiated protein foods. Third, identify any changes in the functional properties (e.g., emulsifying ability, water binding ability, flavor contribution, elasticity in doughs, texturizing) of irradiated food proteins.

Research has shown that the irradiation of proteins and amino acids in foods has little or no effect on the biological value of the protein. The values are in fact equivalent to those obtained for nonirradiated controls. Biological value is the percentage of nitrogen absorbed that is actually used by a living organism for growth and other functions specific to proteins. Experimental data on the digestibility (actual availability) of a variety of protein food sources (including beef, milk, and beans) irradiated between 30 and 100 kGy showed no significant change in their digestibility. Amino acid analyses of irradiated (at 3 and 6 kGy) and nonirradiated chicken stored for 6 days at 5°C (41°F) and then cooked showed no significant losses in amino acids due to the irradiation treatment. In addition, there were no decreases in available lysine or declines in the protein efficiency ratio (evidences of protein quality being maintained).[37]

Table 3.5.   Irradiation effects on proteins

Protein Type	Nutritional Effect	Possible Quality and Functional Effect
Amino acids	1, 3	10
Polypeptides	1, 2, 3, 4, 5, 6	4, 5, 7, 8, 9, 10
Enzymes	7	7

KEY: 1 = destruction due to deamination, decarboxylation, or breakage of side chain; 2 = production of amino acids due to peptide bond splitting; 3 = production of amino acid radicals, ammonia; 4 = cross-linking; 5 = denaturation; 6 = formation of protein aggregates; 7 = activation, deactivation, or no effect; 8 = altered water binding capacity; 9 = altered gelling, emulsifying, and foaming properties; 10 = formation of flavored compounds.

Studies have generated data showing no effect of 1 kGy irradiation on the in vitro digestibility of rapeseed protein (an animal feed).[2] Dehydrated onion powder irradiated 4.0-40.0 kGy showed some differences in the quantity of amino acids only at the highest doses; the amino acids in the dry onion powder state were essentially stable to radiolysis.[12] Soybeans irradiated at 1-3 kGy showed changes in protein patterns which suggested that some of the larger subunits that resulted from protein degradation were able to aggregate and combine, though the total protein content of the irradiated soybeans did not change. Protein solubility (ability to interact with and dissolve in water) was decreased in the irradiated soybeans.[11]

A variety of plant seeds (maize, wheat, chickpea, and mung bean) that were irradiated at 0.5-5.0 kGy demonstrated losses of the sulfur-containing amino acids methionine and cysteine (mung bean) especially, as well as the amino acids lysine, phenylalanine, tyrosine, and isoleucine in the other cultivars. The amount of available lysine, however, was increased, and the overall nutritional losses were judged to be minor.[22] Peanut kernels irradiated at 2.5-20.0 kGy and stored for 1 year at either ambient or frozen (−14°C or 6.8°F) temperature exhibited no difference in protein patterns due to irradiation.[8] No increased destruction of amino acids was observed when chilled or frozen broiler chickens were irradiated at doses ranging from 0.5 to 10.0 kGy in another study.[15]

From these and other studies, it has been concluded that the application of low to medium doses of irradiation (<1 to 10 kGy) causes changes in proteins and amino acids similar to those observed with traditional preservation methods, although nutritional quality remains very high. Enzymes are mostly unaffected by these lower doses. Application of the low doses is recommended in order to minimize potential for changes in protein functional properties.

LIPIDS

Lipids (fats and oils) are composed of the same three elements—carbon, hydrogen, and oxygen—as are carbohydrates. The basic form of lipid is called the triglyceride, which consists of a small compound named glycerol attached to three longer fatty acid side chains. As was the case with the protein amino acids, it is the length and chemical makeup of the side chains of the fatty acids that make triglycerides different from one another.

When the fatty acid portion of the side chain is fully bonded along its length with hydrogen, then we refer to a "saturated" fat or triglyceride. If it does not contain a complete complement of hydrogen atoms, a side chain will form what are termed "double bonds" within itself, and this represents an "unsaturated" fatty acid. Triglycerides containing mostly saturated fatty acid side chains tend to be solid at room temperature, and are generally from animal sources (e.g., beef lard and butter). Those containing mostly unsaturated side chains are usually liquid at room temperature and are mostly of plant origin (e.g., corn oil and olive oil). Exceptions include the unsaturated omega-3 fatty acids found in fish. Lipid molecules called phospholipids also occur in foods, and are similar to triglycerides except that one of the fatty acid side chains is replaced by a phosphorus-containing unit. An example of a phospholipid is lecithin, which is found in eggs. Another form of lipid, found only in foods of animal origin, is cholesterol. Like lecithin, it is also found in eggs, as well as in organ meats such as liver.

Irradiation Effects. Irradiation of lipids induces oxidation, which can trigger the formation of lipid hydroperoxides. The development of rancidity, with undesirable odor and flavor production, then occurs, but only at high doses. Other effects include lipid polymerization, typically seen upon storage at some time following treatment with high doses (hundreds of kGy) of irradiation, and the breakdown of lipids into hydrocarbons, aldehydes, esters, and ketones (Table 3.6).

The fatty acids of broiler chickens irradiated to 3.0 kGy to reduce microbial loads were generally unaffected, except for palmitic and oleic fatty acids, which increased.[19] Irradiation at 1 and 10 kGy decreased the crude lipid and phospholipid content of potatoes, with a more marked effect seen at the higher dose.[27] Gamma irradiation of 20 to 100 kGy caused a decrease in the phospholipid content of soybeans, with increased formation of phosphatidyl choline, phosphatidic acid, and inorganic phosphorus as a result.[14] The steam-distilled volatiles of black pepper irradiated at 10, 20, and 30 kGy were compared, and no system-

Table 3.6.   Irradiation effects on lipids

Lipid Type	Nutritional Effect	Possible Quality and Functional Effect
Triglycerides and fatty acids	1	3
Phospholipids and sterols	2	3
Lipids in foods	1, 2	3, 4

KEY: 1 = production of fatty acid esters, lactones and ketones; 2 = production of fatty acids, esters, aldehydes, ketones; 3 = production of rancidity due to oxidation in presence of O_2; 4 = destruction of polyunsaturated fatty acids.

atic change in the volatile oil content was observed upon storage over a 90 day period.[28] Formation of lipid hydroperoxides in whole egg powder and in egg yolk powder irradiated up to 10 kGy increased significantly with doses of 2.5 kGy and higher if the samples were irradiated in air.[20] Chicken irradiated at 1, 2, and 3 kGy was analyzed for the breakdown of thiobarbituric acid, an indicator of lipid oxidation (the TBA test). No differences were observed between irradiated samples and unirradiated controls in this dose range.[17]

In summary, irradiation of lipids can give rise to peroxide formation, which can lead to rancidity (off odors and flavors) in some products, along with a host of other chemical reactions including hydrolysis, polymerization, and crosslinking. The unsaturated fatty acid-containing lipids are more prone to oxidation, and storage of irradiated lipids in an oxygen environment leads to enhanced rancidity. Removal of oxygen during irradiation will inhibit the oxidation of lipids. This can be achieved by packaging the food or oil in an oxygen-free container or by irradiating under vacuum. The oxidation of lipids can also be greatly reduced by protecting the food samples to be irradiated from light, and by adding antioxidant chemicals to them. Antioxidants such as alpha tocopherol, propyl gallate, and butylated hydroxianisole (BHA) have been used traditionally in food processing. When irradiation doses in the low to medium range are used, the number of unsaturations (double bonds) generally remains unchanged during and after treatment. Also, the viscosities of fats and oils are not altered, nor is the caloric value or assimilation of lipids changed. The chemical changes occurring in lipids due to irradiation can also be minimized by applying the treatment to frozen samples.

VITAMINS

Vitamins also contain the element carbon, as do proteins, carbohydrates, and lipids. But they differ in several ways from these macronutrients. Vitamins are small molecules and are not found in large amounts in foods, hence the descriptor "micronutrients". They are classified according to their ability to dissolve in either water or fat, and are so termed. There are thirteen essential vitamins: the water-soluble class—thiamin or B1, riboflavin or B2, niacin or B3, pantothenic acid or B5, pyridoxine or B6, cyanocobalamin or B12, folacin, biotin, and ascorbic acid or vitamin C; and the fat-soluble class—retinol or vitamin A, cholecalciferol or vitamin D, tocopherol or vitamin E, and phylloquinone or vitamin K.

Irradiation Effects. Studies over the last four decades have sought to determine the effects of irradiation on vitamins. While some of the research has focused on pure solutions of vitamin preparations, many studies have investigated effects seen in whole foods. In general, when vitamins are exposed to levels of irradiation sufficient to cause some losses due to destruction, this is because bonds are broken in the vitamin molecules themselves, which produces inactive vitamin fragments. Additionally, antioxidant vitamins can combine with free radicals and lose their vitamin activity, or free radicals and their products can attack and destroy vitamin structure or activity. However, certain vitamins have been found to be quite resistant to irradiation-induced destruction. These include vitamin B12, folacin, and pantothenic acid. The situation with vitamin solutions is a generally negative one, with much destruction due to irradiation taking place. This is often not the case with the same vitamins present in foods, though. It has been proposed that there exist in foods some protective mechanisms to prevent the destruction of vitamins by certain energy processes such as irradiation, either through shielding by surrounding molecular structures or by the presence of protein antioxidants.

The water-soluble vitamins thiamin and ascorbic acid are the least resistant to effects caused by irradiation, although the situation with vitamin C is a rather interesting one. Vitamin C is converted into dehydroascorbic acid by irradiation, yet this compound possesses an activity level nearly equivalent to that of the ascorbic acid form, so losses of this vitamin can actually be quite minimal. Thiamin loss is thought to be due to the indirect effects caused by free radical reactions. Of the other water-soluble vitamins, niacin and pyridoxine are relatively more resistant to irradiation-induced damage, while of the fat-soluble vitamins, only vitamins A and E seem to be affected to any degree by irradiation.

For a time researchers felt that vitamins that were irradiated in solution were damaged to a much greater degree than vitamins intact in foods. More recently, it has been recognized that while some vitamins in certain foods studied were being protected from irradiation degradation by a host of factors, it is not a simple matter to be able to predict that in any given food the same situation will prevail. For pure solutions of the B vitamin group, it was found that comparable vitamin destruction occurred at 5 kGy for riboflavin, 2.5 kGy for nicotinamide (niacin), 0.6 kGy for pyridoxine, and 15 kGy for both thiamin and folic acid.[5]

The stability of B vitamins in irradiated foods as opposed to model systems has also been investigated. Thiamin content of pork irradiated at doses ranging from 2.5 kGy to 75 kGy decreased with increasing irradiation doses, but thiamin retention increased when the temperature for irradiation was lowered to −45°C (−49°F).[38] Studies on cooked chicken have shown only slight decreases in thiamin and vitamin E at the 6 kGy dose level, while studies with irradiated fruits (tangerines, oranges, tomatoes, and papayas) using irradiation doses up to 3 kGy showed little or no effect on vitamin C retention. Ninety percent of thiamin, riboflavin, and niacin was retained in wheat irradiated at either 0.2 or 2.0 kGy. The nutritive quality of bread made from flour irradiated in the range of 0.3 to 0.5 kGy was the same as for controls. Studies with milk and dairy products showed losses of roughly 50% of vitamins A and E, though it has been demonstrated that the addition of ascorbic acid can minimize these losses. Carotene, the vitamin A precursor in foods, was examined in mangos and red capsicums irradiated at 0.075, 0.3, and 0.6 kGy. No significant differences between unirradiated controls and irradiated treatments was observed for this vitamin.[26] Freshly milled rice bran irradiated at 5, 15, or 50 kGy and stored for up to 365 days at ambient temperature was analyzed for vitamin E (tocopherol) content. Tocopherol content decreased with increasing dose, up to 90% during the storage period.[31]

From the data available on this subject, it is clear that vitamins are sensitive to degradative loss due to irradiation, just as they are to heating and other processes. The magnitude of sensitivity varies from vitamin to vitamin, product to product, and treatment condition to treatment condition. In order to retain vitamins in foods that are to be irradiated, low treatment doses combined with cold sample temperatures plus oxygen and light exclusion are recommended.

Detection of Irradiated Foods

The need for a simple yet accurate means to detect whether or not a food has been irradiated exists primarily for the benefit of the purchaser of food (which could be a country which imports what another has produced, the individual grocery retailer who is the middleman in the producer/seller/consumer chain, or the one who ultimately purchases the food to eat it—the consumer. The consumer has every right and reason to make an informed choice in food purchases, or more simply, should have the freedom to choose whether or not to purchase any food. Since the irradiation of foods has been a controversial issue to some consumers, it is important that consumers be able to clearly distinguish between irradiated and nonirradiated foods. Labeling irradiated products with the green radura symbol would identify foods in this way.

From a regulatory control standpoint, it is desirable to be able to verify that a food has received irradiation treatment, as a check on information provided by the food supplier. As a matter of procedure to benefit the consumer, it would also be helpful to be able to check, for instance, that unmarked foods have indeed not received irradiation treatment. For these reasons, and in order to make it possible to enforce legislation requiring irradiation labels on irradiated foods, scientists have sought to develop a test method which is both simple and uniquely applicable to these products.

Since the irradiation procedure as approved for the various food commodities at present does not create any outward physical changes in food shape, appearance, or temperature, nor are they ever likely to, scientists have had to focus on identifying and isolating the minute changes caused in the component food molecules by the process. This is further complicated by the fact that conventional processing methods create most of the same reaction products (i.e., free radicals, radiolytic products, etc.). A recent comprehensive review containing roughly 200 references now exists for the subject of the detection of irradiated food.[13] In our discussion, three methods will be examined: the detection of free radicals, the enumeration of nonviable organisms, and the measurement of DNA breakdown products.

It makes sense to search for radiolytic products and free radicals in foods which have been processed, whether by heat or irradiation, since these are formed if sufficient ionizing energy is used and substrates are present. Many studies have been carried out on irradiated meats, and one interesting outcome is that the detection of lipid-derived radiolytic products offers a good indication of irradiation. Furthermore, it is believed that a direct relationship exists between a radiolytic product and the amount of its "parent" component in the food.[25] A recent investigation of irradiated chicken (0, 5, and 10 kGy) involved the extraction of the total fat in chicken skin. This was followed by chromatographic separation and identification of two radiolytic hydrocarbons that were found only in the irradiated samples. It was also possible in this study to determine which samples had received the 5 kGy dose and which ones the 10 kGy dose.[32] This is because of the linear relationship between the amounts of precursor hydrocarbons present and the amounts of their degradative radiolytic (hydrocarbon) endproducts.

Since irradiation destroys microorganisms contaminating food, it is reasonable to propose a method to detect killed organisms ("nonviable") in a food as proof that it has been irradiated. The DEFT/APC ratio is one such method. DEFT/APC stands for direct epifluorescent filter technique to aerobic plate count ratio. The original microbial "load" (number of contaminating organisms) is determined by the DEFT method, and this quantity is compared to the viable number of organisms left following irradiation. If there is a substantial difference in counts (indicative of the destruction of many microorganisms), the food tests positive for irradiation.[33]

The killing of microorganisms by irradiation treatment stems from the damage done to the DNA of the microorganisms. It is a fundamental supposition, then, to expect to be able to identify microorganisms with damaged DNA in irradiated foods. DNA is composed of the nucleotide bases adenine, guanine, cytosine, and thymidine. A method to quantify traces of damaged thymidine products in whole food homogenates using immunoassay techniques is under development.[9]

Other methods, including electron spin resonance, luminescence, and volatile analysis, have been proposed as detection methods to identify irradiated foods. In conclusion, to date there is still no single test which can unequivocally point out that any food reaction product being detected could only have been caused by irradiation. Current wisdom dictates that a combination of procedures will stand as the rule for determining whether or not a food has received a dose of irradiation energy.

The Quality of Irradiated Foods

The concept of quality, while all important, is a difficult one to define, because of differing perspectives and expectations (e.g., consumer vs. producer or manufacturer). The idea of quality in food is further complicated if one admits that there is a basic difference between raw, unprocessed foods and processed or manufactured foods. What would be accepted as a quality product for the former (e.g., an orange, perhaps with a faded orange color to the peel, that nevertheless has incredibly satisfying flavor, tanginess, amount of pulp, and moisture when consumed) might not be to the latter (e.g., a piece of orange confection that is noticeably less brilliant in color than others in the same batch, meaning it probably will not even reach the consumption stage).

Table 3.7 lists a sampling of quality attributes and potential undesirable changes which can occur to compromise food quality. From this table, a definition for quality emerges. A quality food is one which demonstrates the attributes of safety, nutritional value, color, flavor, and texture in a favorable rather than unfavorable manner to the consumer.

Processes which introduce undesirable changes to the quality attributes of food result in decreased consumer acceptance.[13] Undesirable changes can result from the effects of processing and preservation procedures, including irradiation, if the processes are severe enough. As we have seen throughout this chapter, there are certain reactions which be-

Table 3.7. Food attributes and adverse changes which compromise quality

Attribute	Undesired Change
Safety	Loss of safety due to: microbial contamination; presence of harmful additive
Nutritional value	Loss of activity of any essential nutrient value (essential amino acids, fatty acids, vitamins, minerals)
Color	Loss of original color; development of off color
Flavor	Loss of original flavor; development of off flavor
Texture	Loss of desired texture
Consumer acceptibility	Loss of acceptibility

fall the components of foods during and after the time they are irradiated, and these can contribute to undesirable changes. The degradative reactions include browning, hydrolysis (breakdown) of saccharides, hydrolysis and oxidation of lipids, protein hydrolysis, cross-linking and denaturation, and others. Some of these undesirable changes can be measured both objectively and, most of the time, subjectively.

The subjective assessment of foods is referred to as sensory analysis or sensory evaluation. In sensory evaluation, the sum total of the subjective assessments of all the food attributes merge to create an overall impression of quality. Because of this, sensory evaluation is a most powerful analytical tool in determining food quality.

With respect to irradiated foods, it is important to determine whether the effects of irradiation cause a deficiency in any food attribute, since this could be extremely important from both health (nutrient losses) and marketing (lack of consumer acceptance due to changes in flavor, appearance, and texture) viewpoints. A subtle but important point is that although a particular irradiation treatment (a certain dose delivered under certain conditions) may result in a desired beneficial objective (e.g., destruction of spoilage organisms), this alone is not enough, since the irradiation treatment may also cause an unwanted attribute change. There must be a benefit concommitant with insignificant attribute deterioration in order for a food to remain desirable to the consumer.

In sensory evaluation, panelists rate foods for specific characteristics as detailed in the testing procedure. The evaluations are pooled and statistically analyzed, and conclusions are drawn by the investigators based upon the test results. Many such tests have been performed on irradiated foods, and some of the findings follow. The eating quality of native egg solids, as well as scrambled eggs and mayonnaise made from the egg solids, was found to be indistinguishable from samples irradiated in air to 3.0 kGy and in the absence of oxygen to 5.0 kGy.[21] Sensory evaluation of irradiated (at 1 kGy) fish flesh color and flavor were conducted after 5 days of storage. Panelists were unable to detect flavor differences between controls and irradiated test samples.[23] In another study with fish, it was discovered that a 1-kGy dose could extend the shelf life of various marine species including mackerel, whiting and prawn, without adversely affecting sensory quality. Sensory quality (odor, appearance, flavor, texture, and overall acceptability) decreased as irradiation approached the 5-kGy dose.[29] Vacuum-packaged pork loins irradiated at 1 kGy showed minimal sensory changes with no detectable differences between treated and control samples after 14 days of storage.[24] Frankfurters irradiated from 0.5 to 10 kGy at two temperatures of irradiation [2°C (35.6°F) and −30°C (−22°F)] generally resulted in the same product quality, with no significant difference in tenderness, freshness, off flavor, or overall acceptability.[3]

In our own laboratory, we have conducted several studies to determine whether consumers can detect a difference between irradiated and unirradiated ground beef patties. In the first trial, we conducted a Triangle Test of Difference, where the sensory panelists were asked to evaluate three broiled ground beef patty samples. The panelists were told that, of the group of three samples, two were identical and one was different from the other two, in terms of having been irradiated or not. The doses we chose were 2 kGy and 5 kGy, with the raw ground beef patties being irradiated in the frozen state and packaged under either air or vacuum. Panelists were only able to detect a difference between the samples when the patties were irradiated under air, with no difference detected when the samples were irradiated under vacuum. In a second study conducted to determine the nature of the difference detected by the panelists in the Triangle Test, panelists were served broiled ground beef patty samples irradiated the same way as before, but this time they were asked to evaluate them according to flavor, texture, juiciness, and off-flavor, as well as to choose the sample they preferred. The only significant difference between irradiated and unirradiated patties was in texture and juiciness, with the irradiated samples being rated as more tender and juicy than the unirradiated samples. There was no significant difference in preference, with irradiated patties being preferred as often as unirradiated ones. We are currently conducting additional studies to determine the optimum conditions of temperature, packaging atmosphere, packaging material, and time between irradiation and serving that will yield ground beef patties with the highest quality attributes. Given that irradiated patties have been rated as superior in terms of tenderness and juiciness, it is conceivable to produce by irradiation a patty of exceptionally high quality that may be preferred by consumers over unirradiated samples.

The quality of irradiated foods hinges on consumer acceptance. As approval for various irradiated foods is being granted, it remains important to continue to obtain both trained panelist perception of sensory attributes (appearance, texture, flavor) and consumer panel acceptance of the irradiated foods. In addition, irradiated foods must continue to be analyzed and examined using the latest physical and chemical methods of objective analysis, in order to ensure that the quality of irradiated foods is never in doubt.

Summary and Conclusions

After a considerable amount of research over the past 40 years, it is apparent from reviewing the scientific literature on the subject of food irradiation as applied to food quality that this process deserves a place alongside the more traditional preservation methods such as canning, drying, and freezing. If the lowest effective irradiation dose (Table 3.8) is properly selected according to the particular food product and specific purpose for irradiation, and control of the ambient conditions, including the removal of oxygen and light, plus treatment at low temperature are realized, then any adverse effects of the ionizing energy on the nutrients of the foods can be minimized, if not eliminated. The benefits gained from the *intelligent* application of irradiation to foods include extending shelf life and preventing disease; this actually results in a "value-added" quality product for the consumer.

Food irradiation need not supersede current food processing and

Table 3.8. Effect of experimental food irradiation doses (kGy) for various foods

Product	Dose	(Effect)
Potatoes	0.075	Sprout inhibition
Flour	0.5	Insect disinfestation
Meat and fish	10.0	Pasteurization
Fruits	24.0	Heat inactivation of enzymes

preservation techniques, although it does offer some advantages over other methods in terms of avoiding postprocessing contamination and minimizing organoleptic changes. In fact, current research seeks to explore ways in which the process of food irradiation can be combined with other treatments, each at lower intensities than would be required separately, to accomplish positive and desirable objectives in the realm of food processing and disease control. This is one of the areas where the future of this technology belongs. Once the use of food irradiation is realized, a safe and wholesome food supply for future generations can be assured.

References

1. Auda, H. and coworkers. 1980. Effect of gamma irradiation on the sugar and protein composition of Iraqi dates. In Food Preservation by Irradiation, Vol. 1 (Proceedings: International Symposium, Wageningen, Nov. 1977), p. 459. IAEA.

2. Badshah, A. and coworkers. 1993. Effect of irradiation and other processing methods on in vitro digestibility of rapeseed protein. J. Sci. Food Agric. 61: 273-275.

3. Barbut, S. and coworkers. 1988. Research note: Irradiation dose and temperature effects on the sensory properties of turkey frankfurters. Poult. Sci. 67: 1797-1800.

4. Basson, R. 1983a. Advances in radiation chemistry of food and food components—an overview. In P. Elias and A. Cohen, eds. Recent Advances in Food Irradiation. Elsevier Press, Amsterdam, The Netherlands.

5. Basson, R. 1983b. Recent advances in radiation chemistry of vitamins. In P. Elias and A. Cohen, eds. Recent Advances in Food Irradiation. Elsevier Press, Amsterdam, The Netherlands.

6. Bhatty, R., and MacGregor, A. 1988. Gamma irradiation of hulless barley: effect on grain composition, ß-glucans and starch. Cereal Chem. 65 (6): 463-470.

7. CAST. 1989. Ionizing energy in food processing and pest control: II. Council for Agricultural Science and Technology, Report No. 115, Ames, Iowa.

8. Chiou, R. Y.-Y. and coworkers. 1991. Characterization of gamma irradiated peanut kernels stored one year under ambient and frozen conditions. J. Food Sci. 59 (1): 1375-1377.

9. Deeble, D. and coworkers. 1990. Changes in DNA as a possible means of detecting irradiated food. In Food Irradiation and the Chemist. Royal Society of Chemistry Special Publication 86, pp. 57-59. London, United Kingdom.

10. Diehl, J. 1990. Safety of irradiated foods. Marcel Dekker, New York, New York.

11. El-Moneim, A. and coworkers. 1988. Effect of low-dose irradiation on soybean protein solubility, trypsin inhibitor activity, and protein patterns separated by polyacrylamide gel electrophoresis. J. Agric. Food Chem. 36: 810-813.

12. Galetto, W. and coworkers. 1979. Irradiation treatment of onion powder: effects on chemical constituents. J. Food Sci. 44 (2): 591-595.

13. Glidewell, S. and coworkers. 1993. Detection of irradiated food: a review. J. Sci. Food Agric. 61: 281-300.

14. Hafez, Y. and coworkers. 1989. Effects of microwave heating and gamma irradiation on phytate and phospholipid contents of soybean (Glycine max. L.). J. Food Sci. 54 (4): 958-962.

15. Hanis, T. and coworkers. 1989. Poultry meat irradiation- effect of temperature on chemical changes and inactivation of microorganisms. J. Food Prot. 52: 26-29.

16. Hayashi, T. and coworkers. 1994. Irradiation effects on pepper starch viscosities. J. Food Sci. 59 (1): 118-120.

17. Heath, J. and coworkers. 1990. Effect of high-energy electron irradiation of chicken meat on thiobarbituric acid values, shear values, odor and cooked yield. Poult. Sci. 69: 313-319.

18. Joint FAO/WHO/IAEA Expert Committee. 1981. Wholesomeness of irradiated food. Report No. 659. World Health Organization, Geneva, Switzerland.

19. Katta, S. and coworkers. 1991. Effect of gamma irradiation of whole chicken carcasses on bacterial loads and fatty acids. J. Food Sci. 56 (2): 371-372.

20. Katusin-Razem, B. and coworkers. 1992. Radiation-induced oxidative changes in dehydrated egg products. J. Agric. Food Chem. 40: 662-668.

21. Katusin-Razem, B. and coworkers. 1989. Chemical and organoleptic properties of irradiated dry whole egg and egg yolk. J. Food Prot. 52 (11): 781-786.

22. Khattak, A. and Klopfenstein, C. 1989. Effect of gamma irradiation on the nutritional quality of grains and legumes. II. Changes in amino acid profiles and available lysine. Cereal Chem. 66 (3): 171-172.

23. Liu, M.-S. and coworkers. 1991 Effect of gamma irradiation on the keeping quality and nutrients of Taliapa (*Oreochromis mossambicus*) and Silver

Carp (*Hypophthalmichthys molitrix*) stored at 1°C. J. Sci. Food Agric. 57: 555-563.

24. Mattison, M. and coworkers. 1986. Effect of low dose irradiation of pork loins on the microflora, sensory characteristics and fat stability. J. Food Sci. 51 (2): 284-287.

25. Merrit, C. and coworkers. 1985. A quantitative comparison of the yields of radiolysis products in various meats and their relationship to precursors. J. Amer. Oil Chem. Soc. 62: 708-713.

26. Mitchell, G. and coworkers. 1990. Effect of gamma irradiation on the carotene content of mangos and red capsicums. J. Food Sci. 55 (4): 1185-1186.

27. Mondy, N. and Gosselin, B. 1989. Effect of irradiation on discoloration, phenols and lipids of potatoes. J. Food Sci. 54 (4): 982-984.

28. Piggot, J. and Othman, Z. 1993. Effect of irradiation on volatile oils of black pepper. Food Chem. 46: 115-119.

29. Poole, S. and coworkers. 1994. Low dose irradiation affects microbiological and sensory quality of sub-tropical seafood. J. Food Sci. 59 (1): 85-87; 105.

30. Sabularse, V. and coworkers. 1992. Physicochemical characteristics of brown rice as influenced by gamma irradiation. J. Food Sci. 57 (1): 143-145.

31. Shin, T. and Godber, J. 1994. Tocopherols, tocotrienols, and oryzanol in rice bran affected by microwave or gamma irradiation stabilization and storage relative to oxidative degradation. In IFT 1994 Annual Meeting Book of Abstracts, p. 35. IFT, Chicago, Illinois.

32. Sjöberg, A-M. and coworkers. 1992. Evaluation of a gas chromatographic method for detection of irradiation of chicken and a chicken meat product. J. Sci. Food Agric. 59: 65-75.

33. Sjöberg, A-M. and Manninen, M. 1991. Spices, irradiation, and detection methods. In Potential New Methods of Detection of Irradiated Food (report EUR 13331), pp. 74-85. Commission of the European Communities, Luxembourg.

34. Stone, H. and coworkers. 1991. The Importance of sensory analysis for the evaluation of quality. Food Tech. 45 (6): 88-95.

35. Swallow, J. 1991. Wholesomeness and safety of irradiated foods. In M. Friedman, ed. Nutritional and Toxicological Consequences of Food Processing, pp. 11-31. Plenum Press, New York, New York.

36. Taub, I. and coworkers. 1976. Chemistry of hydrated muscle proteins irradiated at −40°C. Proc. Army Science Conference III, p. 289. West Point, Pennsylvania.

37. Thomas, M. 1988. Use of ionizing radiation to preserve food. In E. Karmas and R. S. Harris, eds. Nutritional Evaluation of Food Processing, pp. 457-490. Van Nostrand Rinehold, New York, New York.

38. Thomas, M. and coworkers. 1981. Effect of radiation and conventional processing on the thiamin content of pork. J. Food Sci. 46: 824-828.

Selected Readings

Elias, P. and Cohen, A., eds. 1977. Radiation Chemistry of Major Food Components. Elsevier Press. Amsterdam, The Netherlands.

Fennema, O, ed. 1985. Food Chemistry. Marcel Dekker, Inc. New York.

Giddings, G. G. 1985. An industrial view of commercial food irradiation. In Food Irradiation Processing, proceedings of an international symposium organized by the IAEA and the WHO. International Atomic Energy Agency. Vienna, Austria.

Institute of Food Technologists Symposium. 1989. Food irradiation: a most versatile 20th century technology for tomorrow. Food Tech. 43 (7): 75-97.

International Consultative Group on Food Irradiation. 1991. Facts about food irradiation. International Atomic Energy Agency. Vienna, Austria.

Josephson, E. S. 1983. Preservation of food by ionizing radiation. CRC Press. Boca Raton, Florida.

Josephson, E. S., Thomas, M. H., and Calhoun, W. K. 1978. Nutritional aspects of food irradiation: An overview. J. Food Proc. Pres. 2: 299-313.

Murray, T. K. 1983. Nutritional aspects of food irradiation. In P. S. Elias and A. J. Cohen, (Eds.) Recent Advances in Food Irradiation, pp. 203-216. Elsevier Biomedical Press, Amsterdam, The Netherlands.

Pennfield, M. and Campbell, A. 1990. Experimental Food Science. Academic Press. San Diego, California.

CONSUMER ACCEPTANCE OF IRRADIATED FOODS

STEPHEN G. SAPP, Ph.D

Introduction

Given that food irradiation is a process that has been proven to be both safe and effective in eliminating microorganisms of public health importance, the only barrier to widespread commercial application of food irradiation is consumer acceptance. Currently, just very small amounts of irradiated food are sold in America. But irradiation processing for many commodities has been approved by the U.S. Food and Drug Administration (FDA), and when enough consumers express a desire for irradiated food, industry representatives say they will respond. Industry response has taken some time because groups opposed to food irradiation have been successful in in frightening initially uncertain consumers and convincing some legislative bodies that most persons do not want the process. Successful advocacy by opposition groups has angered members of the scientific community and representatives of health organizations worldwide because they think opposition groups use false and misleading statements to frighten consumers for political and financial gain. Food industry representatives cannot anticipate the outcome of this controversy and therefore are reluctant to promote food irradiation for fear of backlash by angry consumers. The controversy has prompted much media attention. A cycle is created wherein the controversy makes good press, which in turn reinforces the perception of potential hazards to consumers and heightens the visibility of opposition groups. The resulting stalemate in consumer acceptance has hindered the rapid adoption of food irradiation. Recent outbreaks of foodborne illness, however, have resulted in renewed interest in this technology by the food industry and legislators, and by consumers looking for solutions to the problem of food safety.

This chapter reviews consumer concerns about food irradiation and the debate being waged by the scientific community and advocacy groups opposed to the process.[14] It discusses existing approaches to consumer education with respect to communication strategies that emphasize the importance of evaluating risk acceptance within the context of social, political, and economic conditions. The chapter argues that the resolution of consumer apprehension will require more than education on scientific findings about food irradiation because apprehension is based on broader issues than education, such as consumers' trust in the ability of government agencies to regulate safety, their concerns about current food production and processing techniques, and their philosophies about what constitutes acceptable risk. The chapter closes with suggestions for addressing consumer concerns about food irradiation.

Current Status of Food Irradiation in the United States

GOVERNMENTAL REGULATIONS ON FOOD IRRADIATION

The FDA has approved irradiation for wheat and wheat powder, white potatoes, spices and dry vegetable seasonings, dry or dehydrated enzyme preparations and aromatic vegetable substances, pork, fresh fruits, and poultry. The World Health Organization (WHO), the Food and Agriculture Organization (FAO), and the International Atomic Energy Association (IAEA) support food irradiation as a means of preserving food and reducing food poisoning. Food irradiation has been endorsed by health organizations, international committees, and scientific societies worldwide and is approved for use in 36 countries for over 50 different foods.

The FDA approved food irradiation under provisions of the Food Additives Amendment of the Federal Food, Drug, and Cosmetic Act, which requires sufficient evidence be presented to FDA officials for them to determine, with reasonable certainty, that no harm will result from eating irradiated food.[20] Substantial technical knowledge and experience are required to determine what constitutes sufficient evidence for concluding with reasonable certainty that a process or additive is safe. Traditionally, regulations rely upon findings from animal feeding studies. Such studies, however, can be inadequate indicators of the safety of irradiated food. Typically, animal feeding studies operate under the premise of judging the toxicity of a substance by its effects on animal health when fed in large doses. Irradiation, however, is not a substance in the food that can be fed in large doses; it is a process that affects the food as a whole. Attempts to feed exaggerated amounts of irradiated food to animals can be misleading, therefore, because adverse effects can occur due to the exaggerated diet itself, having nothing to do with the effects of irradiation.

Recognizing the difficulty of interpreting animal feeding studies, the FDA in 1979 established the Bureau of Foods Irradiated Food Committee (BFIFC), consisting of six scientists with expertise in toxicology, nutrition, chemistry, and regulatory issues, to evaluate the safety of irradiated food. The committee concluded that no further toxicological testing was required for foods irradiated at doses below 1 kGy or for ingredients constituting less than 0.01% of the diet irradiated at doses up to 50 kGy.

Then, in 1981, after considering recommendations of the Joint FAO/IAEA/WHO Expert Committee on the Wholesomeness of Irradiated Food, the FDA established the Irradiated Foods Data Task Group (i.e., the Codex Alimentarius Commission: Codex) to review available toxicological studies. Codex established criteria to evaluate all existing studies, reviewed studies deemed appropriate for their consideration, and concluded that results from sound scientific studies showed no adverse toxicological effects from eating irradiated food.

The FDA based its decision on available data and proposed to permit irradiation at doses up to 1 kGy to inhibit maturation of fresh fruits and vegetables and for insect disinfestation. Also, the FDA proposed to establish a dose limit of 30 kGy for dry spices and seasonings. The FDA received over 5,000 comments concerning this proposal. Pauli reports that very few of the comments raised specific, substantive issues worthy of further scientific study; but an overwhelming number of comments asked for labeling requirements.[20] The FDA subsequently included in its 1986 regulation a requirement that labels for irradiated foods include a "radura" symbol. Also the FDA required a statement on the label such as "Treated with Radiation" or "Treated by Irradiation" to allow time for the radura symbol to become recognized. In 1990, the FDA approved irradiation to control illness-causing microorganisms (e.g., *Salmonella*) in poultry.

In addition to the FDA, the Food Safety and Inspection Service (FSIS) and the Animal and Plant Health Inspection Service (APHIS) regulate the irradiation of some foods. The FSIS further regulates irradiation processing of animal products such as pork and poultry, and APHIS further regulates irradiation processing for quarantine treatments such as for various types of fruit flies. Commercial application of food irradiation must conform also to regulations set by the U.S. Nuclear Regulatory Commission when using radioactive source materials, by the Department of Transportation if transporting hazardous materials, and by the Occupational Safety and Health Administration for worker safety.

Pauli speculates that this multiplicity of agency regulations can sometimes present a bewildering barrier to firms interested in food irradiation.[20] He points out also that a new technology must demonstrate a relative economic advantage to be commercially successful. Most previous research, however, has been government sponsored and "product" oriented—focusing on safety and wholesomeness—rather than "profit" oriented. Governmental regulations offer little guidance, therefore, on whether commercial application of food irradiation is economically feasible. However, recent studies (discussed in Chapter 5) point to consumer's willingness to pay more for irradiated food, once given information on its benefits.

OPPOSITION TO FOOD IRRADIATION

Few consumer products have received the amount and intensity of opposition from advocacy groups that food irradiation has. Organizations opposed to food irradiation, such as Food & Water, Inc. (which subsumed activities of the former National Coalition to Stop Food Irradiation) and The Center for Science in the Public Interest, have influenced legislators in nine states (Alaska, Hawaii, Illinois, Maine, Massachusetts, New Jersey, New York, Oregon, and Pennsylvania) to consider banning the sale of irradiated products. Three states (Maine, New Jersey, and New York) have either banned or issued moratoriums on the sale of irradiated food (excluding foods containing irradiated ingredients such as spices). The sale of irradiated food has been banned in some countries (Australia, Federal Republic of Germany, and New Zealand), and the European Community requires strict labeling of irradiated foods and any irradiated ingredients.[11] In 1987, the General Assembly of the International Organization of Consumers Unions (IOCU) demanded a worldwide moratorium on the further use and development of food irradiation pending satisfactory resolution of consumer issues and concerns.[12]

The activities of opposition groups have provided a focal point for hundreds of articles and editorials in magazines, newspapers, and scientific journals concerning the advisability of using irradiation to treat food. Television documentaries and talk shows in the United States have interviewed central figures in the food irradiation controversy and offered their opinions on the safety the technology. The amount of attention devoted to the food irradiation controversy, as well as the well-organized efforts of opposition groups to mobilize letter-writing campaigns to legislators and representatives of commodity groups and retail food chains, has prompted some representatives of the food industry to state they will not promote or sell irradiated food.

Scientists argue that opponents hold an advantage in influencing public opinion because their statements do not undergo the strict review process of scientific articles. Opponents of food irradiation make inflammatory demands, request unneeded research as a stalling tactic, and apply unwarranted pressure on legislators. Scientists say opposition groups take statements out of context to convince consumers food irradiation lacks sufficient evidence of safety and wholesomeness. Pauli points out that, "because only harm, not its absence, can be demonstrated conclusively, one can always speculate about situations where harm could occur but for which no data exist."[20] Thus, no amount of research can address all questions about food irradiation or determine whether irradiated food is 100% safe to eat, any more than it can determine that cooking or freezing or refrigeration, or any type of food processing is 100% safe.

Consumer Issues Regarding Food Irradiation

This section reviews statements made by members of the scientific community and opposition groups on the central issues of the food irradiation controversy. The issues reviewed derive primarily from articles appearing in *Safe Food News,* a member newsletter distributed by Food & Water, Inc., a leading advocacy group opposed to food irradiation. Responses to these issues were compiled primarily from articles appearing in *Food Technology,* a refereed professional publication of the Institute of Food Technologists.

INDUCED RADIOACTIVITY IN FOOD

Most persons associate the word irradiation with dangerous events such as atomic bomb explosions and nuclear reactor accidents. It is not surprising, therefore, to find consumers skeptical of the safety of irradiated food. Scientific evidence shows that foods do not become radioactive when exposed to ionizing radiation because the exposure times and energy levels of radiation sources approved for foods are not sufficient to induce radioactivity. Even opposition groups reluctantly agree that no residual radiation remains in irradiated food.

THE NEED FOR FOOD IRRADIATION

Opposition groups say irradiation is not needed because other preservation methods are available and because proper handling and cooking can prevent food poisoning given the current quality of the food supply.[31] Scientists,[21] on the other hand, point out that in 1992, *Salmonella* and *Campylobacter* together accounted for an estimated 4 million cases of food poisoning and approximately 1,000-2,000 deaths in the United States. Another organism, *Listeria monocytogenes*, was responsible for more than 1,500 cases of food poisoning and between 378 and 433 deaths.[21] In addition to the human tragedies resulting from these illnesses and deaths, the medical costs associated with food poisoning are estimated by the USDA to range from $3.8 to $4.3 annually.[13]

Scientists point out also that irradiation may offer an alternative to chemical treatments and where other methods are not usually available, such as in Third World countries. Pszczola,[22] for example, argues that irradiation has the potential to solve some food problems that other methods cannot sufficiently address, such as reducing or eliminating pathogen contamination in meats and poultry, offering an alternative to chemical fumigants for fruits and vegetables, controlling postharvest losses due to insects and spoilage, and permitting imports of a broader range of foods.

UNIQUE RADIOLYTIC PRODUCTS

Any process that heats food—such as cooking, exposure to light, or irradiation—creates free radicals, or highly reactive molecules in the food.[22] Opposition groups say irradiation may create unique radiolytic products (URPs) that could be toxic, carcinogenic, or mutagenic. Scientists, however, argue that no radiolytic products have been found in irradiated food that have not also been found in much greater amounts in food exposed to ordinary cooking. Further, no URPs have been found in irradiated foods despite the ability to detect substances down to the part-per-quadrillion level (that is, 1 in 1,000,000,000,000,000!).

NUTRIENT LOSSES IN IRRADIATED FOOD

Opposition groups argue that irradiated food is not as wholesome as unirradiated food because the process depletes vitamins. Studies confirm that up to 56% of ascorbic acid (vitamin C) is lost in the irradiation process. Scientific researchers say this loss is comparable to losses due to conventional processes, such as canning. Studies show that other vitamins, such as niacin, thiamine, riboflavin, and beta-carotene, remain relatively stable after irradiation. Also, research shows that changes in carbohydrates, proteins, and fats are minimal and do not affect the wholesomeness of irradiated food, as proven by over 40 years of research conducted worldwide. For more information on this subject, refer to Chapter 3.

CONCERNS OVER POSSIBLE ABUSES

Opposition groups express concerns that unethical processors may use irradiation to convert low-quality or spoiled products to seemingly high-quality products by masking their off flavor or odor. Ionizing radiation, however, cannot mask the off flavor or odor of spoiled products. If spoiled food tastes or smells bad before irradiation, it will taste or smell bad after irradiation.[24] Similarly, enforcement by regulatory agencies can prevent reirradiation of reinfected products. Opponents have questioned whether microbial mutants, resistant to ionizing irradiation, may be formed, but the Board of the International Committee on Microbiology Societies states that, after years of investigation, there is no scientific evidence to indicate these concerns are valid.[22]

CESIUM-137 AS RADIOACTIVE SOURCE MATERIAL

Opposition groups claim the Department of Energy is pushing irradiation as a means of selling cesium-137, a by-product of nuclear weapons production. Scientists point out that commercial facilities currently use cobalt-60, a source material produced specifically for irradiation, not nuclear reactions.

SAFETY OF IRRADIATION FACILITIES

An issue receiving much attention by opposition groups is the safety of irradiation facilities. They cite instances where improper handling at facilities irradiating medical supplies has resulted in plant employees being exposed to radiation leaks. Opposition groups are concerned that the additional irradiation facilities needed to handle large volumes of food would increase the potential for mismanagement or accidents. They worry also about accidents on the highways when radioactive materials are being transported. Scientists note that facilities have been irradiating medical supplies safely for over 20 years. They point out also that linear accelerators, which essentially are large x-ray machines with no active radiation source, can be used for large-scale commercial applications.

Although the linear accelerator would seem to satisfy concerns about potential exposure to radioactive materials, opponents say accidents can occur with these machines also.[17] The accidents they mention, however, regard overexposure of humans undergoing x-ray treatment, not worker accidents or risks to communities. Ignored was the point that linear accelerators used for food irradiation eliminate the potential for worker or community contamination from radioactive sources. Thus, when opponents had an opportunity to acknowledge that technologies have been developed to significantly address one of their key concerns, they chose instead to introduce a red herring.

SAFETY OF IRRADIATED FOOD

Is irradiated food safe to eat? The scientific evidence says an emphatic "yes." The only study cited by opposition groups to counter the volumes of research showing the wholesomeness of irradiated foods was conducted by India's National Institute of Nutrition, where malnourished children were fed irradiated wheat as a major part of their diet. Subsequent examination of the children showed they had chromosomal abnormalities known as polyploidy. Scientists point out that polyploidy is fairly common among malnourished children. They note also that polyploidy has been known to occur in healthy animals and humans.[24] Thus, the study has been widely criticized on methodological and statistical criteria. Scientists argue that food irradiation has been researched for over 40 years and that numerous animal feeding studies show no indications of adverse effects, prompting the World Health Organization and other agencies throughout the world to declare irradiated foods to be as safe and wholesome as unirradiated food.

CONSUMER DESIRE FOR IRRADIATED FOOD

A central issue for legislators and industry representatives is whether consumers want irradiated food. Opponents have been very successful in organizing letter writing campaigns to convince these persons they would face severe consumer backlash by supporting food irradiation. The validity of this claim can be tested only in the marketplace, but scientists argue that activists are not giving the marketplace a chance to test the claim. By trying to deny consumers a choice, opposition groups are using "terrorist tactics" motivated only by their special interests.[22]

MEDIA ATTENTION TO THE FOOD IRRADIATION DEBATE

Bord[3] reviewed 156 nontechnical books and articles available to the general public and classified them into three broad categories: articles concerning FDA regulations, which tended to focus on the future of the technology and to depict food irradiation in a favorable light; articles in semi-technical and popular science magazines and in newspapers, to express doubts about the technology in language that was guardedly optimistic; and articles in health and environmental publications, which tended to be uniformly negative. He noted that articles in the popular press gave more space to opposition statements, expressed food irradiation in language that clearly was not neutral (e.g., "bombarding bananas," "nuked lunch," "atomic edibles"), and that tended to sensationalize weak arguments made by opponents. Thus, opposition groups often receive too much or too favorable attention by the media, with the media replying that they report controversy rather than create it.

Public Opinion

Public acceptance of new technologies, even ones with clearly recognized benefits and little controversy, can sometimes require several decades of diffusion activities.[23] It is therefore too early to make predictions about whether sufficient numbers of consumers will purchase irradiated food to make the technology commercially feasible. Based upon previous research, however, this section can summarize the most important issues affecting consumer acceptance.

The section reviews three types of studies: opinion polls, laboratory experiments, and market tests. Because most consumers need some education about food irradiation before their opinions can be measured accurately, the methodology used to measure consumer opinions can significantly affect the findings of a study. Due to space and time constraints, opinion polls typically provide less information than laboratory experiments. A laboratory experiment, on the other hand, cannot study a nationwide, representative sample. Polls are best used to measure opinions on well-known topics or awareness about a topic. Laboratory experiments are best used to measure the effects of different variables on uncertain opinions under controlled conditions. Supermarket tests focus primarily on consumers' willingness to purchase or on sensory evaluations of food. Because it is difficult to compare the findings of polls, laboratory experiments, and market tests, the findings of each approach are discussed separately.

FINDINGS FROM OPINION POLLS

Bord[3] points out that good correspondence between survey responses and respondent behavior requires that the time between attitude measurement and behavior be short, that situational conditions favor attitude-behavior correspondence, that attitudes and behavior be measured at the same level of specificity, and that the respondent have well-formed attitudes about the behavior. Failure to meet these criteria can yield inaccurate findings, especially when consumers are uncertain about their opinions.[2] These criteria might not have been met in previous opinion polls because most persons have little knowledge about food irradiation and the information they received prior to the poll might have been biased toward a favorable or unfavorable position. Also, they might not have given sufficient attention to the subject prior to participating in the poll to develop well-formed attitudes.

Findings on consumer awareness have varied widely across different nationwide polls. Wiese[32] found in 1984 that 23% of respondents had heard of food irradiation. Brand Group[7] found in 1986 that 66% of respondents had heard of the process. Schutz et al.[30] found in 1989 that nearly 60% of respondents had heard of food irradiation, but in 1990, Malone[16] found an awareness of only 25% in a nationwide sample. Gallup,[15] in a 1993 poll, found that 73% of consumers had heard of food irradiation, but most respondents said they had a low level of knowledge about the process. Gallup reported that only 5% of their respondents claimed in-depth knowledge about food irradiation. None of these studies measured potential bias in the information known by respondents who had prior knowledge of food irradiation.

Findings on acceptance have been fairly consistent across different opinion polls. Weiss found that 22% said they would purchase irradiated food, 44% were not sure, and 28% said they would not purchase. Brand Group found that 22% said they would definitely try irradiated food, 47% said they would probably try it, 20% said they would probably not try it, and 11% said they would definitely not try it. Schutz et al.[30] found that 15% of their respondents said they were very likely to purchase irradiated food, 30% said they were likely to purchase, 34% were uncertain, 13% were unlikely to purchase, and 9% were very likely not to purchase. Bord and O'Conner[5] found that 14% of Pennsylvania women said they would definitely try irradiated food, 63% would probably try it, 17% said they would probably not try it, and 5% said they would definitely not try it. The Gallup poll found the strongest indication of consumer acceptance. Approximately 54% of respondents said they would likely purchase irradiated meat over nonirradiated meat, and 60% of these persons said they would pay a 5% premium for irradiated hamburger.

The Brand Group has offered a typology for interpreting findings from nationwide polls that conforms with theoretical models of diffusion.[23] They estimate approximately 25-30% of the population favors irradiation but have a tenuous hold on their attitudes. Another 55-65% of the population is undecided about the technology, and the final 5-10% have strong objections about food irradiation. Bord[3] offers both optimistic and pessimistic interpretations of findings from four opinion polls. He notes if the percentages for persons from these polls saying they will try or probably try irradiated food are combined, then 25, 45, 69, and 77% of respondents so indicate, with the larger percentages appearing in more recent studies. On the other hand, only 14, 15, 22, and 25% of respondents express strong postive attitudes. The large percentage of persons expressing uncertainty in opinion polls may be their most important finding. As Bord[3] notes, "It is impossible for people to have a solid set of beliefs about something they know little about." But, in an arena of uncertainty, new information, especially negative information, can create dramatic shifts in consumer opinion. It can reasonably be concluded that most consumers are not strongly opposed to irradiation, but are uncertain and most likely awaiting strongly voiced opinions from persons or organizations they respect and trust.[23]

FINDINGS FROM LAB EXPERIMENTS

Bruhn et al.[9] provided "conventional" and "alternative" consumers with facts about food irradiation without presenting the arguments used by anti-irradiation activists. They then asked the consumers to discuss the technology in small groups. Expert and nonexpert confederates were randomly assigned to lead discussion within groups. Both conventional and alternative consumers expressed more concern about other potential food safety hazards than they did about food irradiation, which supported findings from opinion polls.[18] Conventional consumers were influenced more by experts than were alternative consumers and expressed more willingness to buy irradiated products. Among conventional consumers, prior knowledge of irradiation, pre-experiment concern about irradiation, and age were found to be significant indicators of acceptance. Among alternative consumers, prior knowledge and age significantly affected concern. Age had a significant positive coefficient on concern among conventional consumers but a significant negative coefficient among alternative consumers. Bruhn et al.[9] concluded that consumer acceptance of food irradiation could be increased through educational efforts, particularly by using experts to present information.

Sapp and Harrod[27] allowed some of their subjects in a laboratory experiment time to discuss irradiation after hearing both facts about the technology and opposition arguments. They found that the opinions of subjects in discussion groups were more extreme than those of subjects who were not allowed discussion time. These findings support theories on social persuasion, which state that opinions will polarize as a mechanism of conflict resolution within the group. Previous research shows that negative word of mouth can exert disproportionate influence on consumer opinion. In support of this research, Sapp and Harrod[27] noted that negative comments made during group discussion influenced opinions more than did favorable comments, which implied that normative factors may be important determinants of consumer acceptance of food irradiation.

Bord and O'Conner[4] presented subjects with three types of information, a technical versus nontechnical discussion of food irradiation; an extended discussion of supportive and opposing arguments about the technology (either present or absent); and a discussion of the history of the use of food irradiation (either present or absent). The only manipulation that significantly affected opinions was the discussion of the history of use, which included information about use by astronauts and those with extreme immune deficiencies, which seemed to offer some assurances to uncertain subjects. Bord and O'Conner noted that demographic factors did not have a strong impact on opinions. Although women tended to be more opposed than were men, gender did not significantly affect acceptance after controlling for other variables. The most important factor affecting acceptance was trust in government and industry. Trust accounted for 74% of the explained variance, and accuracy of knowledge accounted for an additional 20% of the explained variance. Participants stressed the uncertainty of the technology and potential misuse by its sponsors as the most important issues affecting their opinions. Also, participants expressed more negative opinions during discussion than on their follow-up questionnaires, which prompted Bord and O'Conner to speculate that it was socially and psychologically "easy" to express concern and that participants might have wanted to appear prudent during the focus group discussions. They concluded that normative factors were more important than technical information in structuring attitudes toward food irradiation.

Sapp et al.[25] provided all their subjects with facts about irradiation, as well as con arguments, and then allowed some subjects time to discuss food irradiation in small groups. They found attitude-behavior consistency for subjects who discussed food irradiation before stating their opinions of and intentions to eat irradiated food, but not for subjects who stated their opinions and intentions without prior discussion with others. They found that trust in government and industry was the most important variable in predicting responses to four measures of acceptance (Opinion of Food Irradiation, Intent to Advocate Against Food Irradiation, Intent to Eat Irradiated Food, and Eating Irradiated Food in a Taste Panel). Trust in government and industry was the only variable with a significant partial effect on participating on the taste panel, and had the highest standardized coefficient in prediction models for all four variables. Sapp et al.[26] found that normative factors (i.e., word of mouth and trust in government and industry) were much more important than demographic factors in predicting consumer acceptance of food irradiation.

FINDINGS FROM MARKET TESTS

Bruhn and Noell[8] conducted in-store demonstrations in 1987 to examine consumer responses to irradiated papayas. Approximately 50% of the persons walking by test areas stopped; the amount of irradiated papayas they purchased was more than 10 times the amount of traditionally treated ones purchased. Diehl[10] reported that more than 2 tons of irradiated mangoes were sold within a week in a Miami Beach, Florida, store in 1990. Pszczola[21] reported four groceries easily sold their initial supplies of irradiated poultry in independent marketings in 1993. These findings indicate that enough consumers will purchase irradiated foods to make the process commercially feasible. Vindicator, Inc., a company based in Mulberry, Florida, began irradiating fresh strawberries in January 1992 and is still in business; but large-scale marketing has yet to take place. An important indicator of commercial feasibility will be the success of Vindicator, Inc.

SUMMARY OF CONSUMER ACCEPTANCE STUDIES

In summary, opinion polls show awareness has increased, but much education still is needed to adequately inform consumers about food irradiation. Polls indicate approximately 25-30% of consumers have initially favorable impressions of food irradiation, approximately 55-65% are uncertain about the process, and 5-10% are opposed to it. Laboratory studies indicate consumer acceptance is highly dependent upon normative factors such as word-of-mouth discussion and trust in the government and industry agencies responsible for the regulation and processing of irradiated food. Market tests indicate consumers will purchase irradiated food if given the chance to do so.

Diffusion research[23] has found that initial adopters of an innovation tend to be demographically and socially different from most of the population, and findings from marketings of irradiated food support this generalization.[21] The potential for large-scale commercial feasibility, therefore, must be interpreted with caution because most consumers are uncertain about food irradiation and susceptible to dramatic shifts in opinion. Innovations, to be widely adopted, usually must be accepted by well-respected opinion leaders. For food irradiation, such leaders may be media such as popular home, food, and even parenting magazines; but this statement is speculative because no research has identified opinion leaders for food irradiation. Other potential opinion leaders are health organizations. Previous research has found, for example, that consumers respond favorably when hearing that food irradiation is endorsed by the American Medical Association.[15]

The Food Irradiation Controversy and Risk Communication Research

This section discusses food irradiation with respect to perspectives on risk assessment and communication. Consumer acceptance may be viewed as an issue of education on the scientific merits of the technology. If consumers can be made aware of the facts about food irradiation, one may argue, then they will adopt the technology. The social construction perspective, however, argues that social, economic, and political considerations must be included in risk communications. Given previous research showing the impact of normative factors on consumer acceptance, the social construction perspective may offer important suggestions for addressing consumer concerns about food irradiation.

PERSPECTIVES ON RISK COMMUNICATION

Much debate focuses on the volume and quality of scientific evidence supporting the safety of irradiated food. Debate focuses also on the quality of assumptions built into assessments of safety and even on the validity of the assessment process itself. Debates on food irradiation thus mirror debates on other areas of food safety and on broader areas of risk assessment. Such debates are not limited to evaluations of scientific validity and reliability, but include philosophical arguments regarding the proper values by which risk should be assessed.

A common suggestion for alleviating consumer concerns about food irradiation is that efforts at education be increased. This suggestion assumes increased education will enable the consumer to better understand the nature of food science and presumably appreciate more fully the safeguards of our food supply. Suggestions that consumers learn more about quantitative risk assessment, food inspection and regulation procedures, and scientific findings regarding food hazards appear in many scientific and governmental publications addressing consumer concerns.

Educational messages alone, however, cannot be expected to alleviate food safety concerns, because what constitutes "education" differs from the perspectives of scientists and opposition groups. Educational messages intended to promote irradiation can heighten concerns when attempting to explain the complex and technical nature of the process. Most importantly, educational messages are delivered within a social context of conflicting values and attitudes regarding appropriate food safety technologies. "At the heart of the food safety debate," states Chemical Feast author James Turner,[1] "is a clash of values." The resulting dilemma is that food safety decisions, and even protocols for making decisions, have become a matter of uncertainty and debate.

Clashes involving value differences are not resolved with presentations of scientific evidence, but must address the credibility of the organizations that produce and evaluate scientific evidence. To opponents of irradiation, scientific, governmental, and industry organizations hold incorrect value systems that bias their interpretations of safety. Within the broader arena of food safety, for example, debates about the viability of the Delaney Amendment focus on whether foods should be completely free of carcinogens or have levels of carcinogens that allow for "acceptable risk." Debates about food irradiation are similar in that misinformed opponents think the process should not be approved and used until research can show it is 100P safe, even though such a level of safety is not present in foods processed by conventional methods, such as home cooking.

The socially constructed notion of risk assumes that truths do not exist independently of people—people who make value judgments, educated guesses, and politically expedient decisions at all phases of the risk identification and assessment process.[6,19] This conceptualization of risk suggests the need for policy structured by negotiating among alternative belief systems held by technicians, policy makers, consumers, consumer advocates, and the media. The social process approach implies that risk communication must involve citizen participation in policy decisions. Scherer and Juanillo[29] for example, state that risk communication should be judged by the extent and quality of public involvement in risk assessment and policy formation, and that both scientific and lay opinions must enter into the risk identification, assessment, and communication process.

A Cornell University sponsored workshop[28] has incorporated the socially constructed perspective of risk into strategies for effective risk identification, assessment, and communication policy. Workshop materials stress that risk policy should be a process, wherein all participants—government, science, industry, mass media, opposition groups, and the lay public—become involved in an interactive exchange of information and philosophy. Such a strategy is thought to support the credibility of all participants, provide mechanisms for all participants to learn from one another, develop systems for identifying information needs, provide the nonscientific community with methods for interpreting data, and develop systems to provide mass media practitioners with accurate and complete information for publication. This strategy, of course, implies that participants interact with honest intentions rather than for the purpose of seeking financial or political gain. Possible strategies scientists can pursue for enabling effective interaction, therefore, include promoting active involvement by citizens' groups, conducting interactive public hearings, and becoming more active in the public forum on food irradiation.

IMPLICATIONS FOR CONSUMER EDUCATION

It may be beneficial to interpret findings from consumer studies within the social process approach to risk communication. Given the low level of consumer knowledge about food irradiation, and the constant bombardment of misinformation from activists opposed to the process, it is necessary to continue providing information about the extensive research on its safety and benefits. This approach by itself, however, will not be sufficient and will need to be complemented by other strategies. Research findings on the importance of trust and group discussion point to a need to broaden the scope of favorable messages about food irradiation.

First, Pszczola[22] suggests that scientists develop closer relationships with the media so emotionalism is not overemphasized compared with scientific facts. He cautions that the lack of stories informing consumers of the advantages of irradiation may be as damaging as bad publicity. Because consumers receive most of their information from the media, it becomes imperative to educate reporters about the science of irradiation and how inflammatory remarks can bias consumer opinions.

Second, Pszczola[22] suggests that educational efforts must be expanded to include health professionals, such as dietitians, home economists, nutritionists, and doctors. As a result of greater outreach activities, health professionals may be better prepared to consider the claims of opposition groups within the context of scientific findings.

Third, Pauli[20] suggests that adoption of food irradiation may require a simultaneous recognition by the industry and the public that irradiation offers a way of improving food safety. Such recognition may depend on the industry and the public seeing the results of actual applications of food irradiation. Irradiation of foods for special audiences, such as persons with immune deficiencies, may not only demonstrate that irradiation can serve real world needs, but also bolster the public's trust in the technology and the agencies that regulate and apply it.

Fourth, statements that directly address the claims and qualifications of opponents are needed to show that the claims are not factual. Government agencies and food processing firms cannot stop irresponsible groups from making scientifically unsound claims about food irradiation. They can, however, actively challenge the qualifications and motivations of such groups.

Fifth, effort is needed to reaffirm the credibility of government and industry organizations responsible for food irradiation. Even the most extensive educational campaign will fail if the sources of information are not trusted. Educational messages, therefore, should address not only the *findings* of research on food irradiation, but also the rigorous procedures and checks involved in *producing and evaluating* research findings by scientists, regulatory agencies, and irradiation processors.

Regardless of the specific type of educational messages employed, scientists must help reaffirm the public's trust in the government and industry organizations responsible for food irradiation. Also, scientists must appreciate the effects on consumer acceptance of word of mouth and endorsements by opinion leaders and therefore more actively state their viewpoints in the types of media from which most consumers receive their information.

References

1. Anonymous. 1986. How safe is our food supply? Prepared Foods 155: 221-240.

2. Ajzen, I. and M. Fishbein. 1980. Understanding Attitudes and Predicting Social Behavior. Englewood Cliffs, NJ: Prentice-Hall. Fazio, R.H. 1986. How do attitudes guide behavior? In: The Handbook of Motivation and Cognition, R.M. Sorrention and E.T. Higgens (Eds.). New York: Guilford Press.

3. Bord, R.J. 1991. Consumer acceptance of irradiation food in the United States. In: Food Irradiation, S. Thorne (Ed.), p. 61. London: Elsevier Applied Science.

4. Bord, R.J. and R. E. O'Conner. 1990. Risk communication, knowledge, and attitudes: explaining reactions to a technology perceived as risky. Risk Analysis. 10: 499.

5. Bord, R.J. and R. E. O'Conner. 1989. Who wants irradiated food?: Untangling complex public opinion. Food Tech. 43: 87.

6. Bradbury, J.A. 1989. The policy implications of differing concepts of risk. Sci. Tech. Hum. Val. 14: 380-389.

7. Brand Group, Irradiated Seafood Product. 1986. Final Report, Brand Group, Chicago, IL.

8. Bruhn, C.M and J. W. Noell. 1987. Consumer in-store response to irradiated papayas. Food Tech. 41: 9.

9. Bruhn, C.M., H. G. Schutz, and R. Sommer. 1986. Attitude change toward food irradiation among conventional and alternative consumers. Food Tech. 40: 86.

10. Diehl, J.F. 1990. Safety of Irradiated Foods. New York: Marcel Decker.

11. Ehlermann, D.A.E. 1991. Current status of food irradiation in Europe. In: Food Irradiation, S. Thorne (Ed.), p. 87. London: Elsevier Applied Science.

12. Feenstra, M.H., and A.H. Scholten. 1991. Consumer acceptance of irradiated foods. In: Food Irradiation, S. Thorne (Ed.), p. 97. London: Elsevier Applied Science.

13. Food Safety and Inspection Service. 1993. Mandatory safe handling statements on labeling of raw meat and poultry products; Interim rule. U.S. Department of Agriculture, Washington, D.C., Federal Register 58(156): 43477-43489.

14. For reviews of the current status of food irradiation, see: S. Thorne (Ed.), Food Irradiation. London: Elsevier Applied Science, 1991. M. Marcotte, "Commercial food irradiation, market tests, and consumer attitudes research—summary tables." Discussion document prepared for the United Nations Environment Programme, Methyl Bromide Technical Options Committee, January 1994. M. Satin, Food Irradiation: A Guidebook. Lancaster, PA: Technomic, 1993.

15. Gallup. 1993. A Survey of Consumers' Awareness, Knowledge, and Attitudes Toward the Process of Irradiation: Summary Report. Princeton, NJ: The Gallup Organization.

16. Malone, J.W. 1990. Consumer willingness to purchase and to pay more for potential benefits of irradiated fresh food products. Agribusiness 6: 163.

17. Morris, M. and M. Colby. 1991. FIN LINK-3, Food Irradiation Network Newsletter. Blairstown, NJ.

18. Opinion Research Corporation. 1988. Trends—Consumer Attitudes and the Supermarket, Washington, DC: Food Marketing Institute.

19. Otway, H. and K. Thomas. 1982. Reflections on risk perception and policy. Risk Anal. 2: 69-82.

20. Pauli, G.H. 1991. Food irradiation in the United States. In: Food Irradiation, S. Thorne (Ed.), p. 235. London: Elsevier Applied Science.

21. Pszczola, D.E. 1993. Irradiated poultry makes U.S. debut in Midwest and Florida markets. Food Tech. 47: 89-96.

22. Pszczola, D.E. 1990. Food irradiation: Countering the tactics and claims of opponents. Food Tech. 44: 92-97.

23. Rogers, E.M. 1983. Diffusion of Innovations, 3d Edition. New York: Free Press.

24. Sahasrabudhe, M.R.. 1990. Food irradiation: Current status, concerns, limitations and future prospects. J. Can. Diet. Assoc. 51: 329-334.

25. Sapp, S.G., W.J. Harrod, and L.Zhao. 1994a. The social construction of consumer risk assessments. J. Home Econ. Consum. Stud. (in press).

26. Sapp, S.G., W.J. Harrod, and L. Zhao. 1994b. Social demographic and attitudinal determinants of consumer acceptance of food irradiation. Agribusiness (in press).

27. Sapp, S.G. and W.J. Harrod. 1990. Consumer acceptance of irradiated food: A study of symbolic adoption. J. Consum. Stud. Home Econ. 14, 133-145.

28. Scherer, C.W. 1990. National Risk Communication Workshop. Department of Communication. Ithaca, NY: Cornell University.

29. Scherer, C.W. and N. K. Juanillo, Jr. 1990. Rationale for interactive risk communication. Part Five In: National Risk Communication Workshop,

C.W. Sherer. Department of Communication. Ithaca, NY: Cornell University.

30. Schutz, H.G., C. M. Bruhn, and K. V. Diaz-Knauf. 1989. Consumer attitudes toward irradiated foods: Effects of labeling and beliefs information. Food Tech. 43: 80.

31. Webb, T., T. Lang, and K. Tucker. 1987. Food Irradiation, Who Wants It? Wellingborough, Great Britain: Thorsons Publishers, 1987. Webb, T. and T. Lang. 1990. Food Irradiation. The Myth and the Reality. Wellingborough, Great Britain: Thorsons Publishers.

32. Weise Research Associates. 1984. Consumer Reaction to the Irradiation Concept. Omaha, NE: Weise Research Associates.

Selected Readings

CAST. 1991 Irradiation of food has the potential to improve human health. NewsCAST 18(3). Ames, IA: Council for Agricultural Science and Technology.

Coon, J. M., E. S. Josephson, and E. Wierbicki. 1985. Food Irradiation. Comments from CAST. Ames, IA: Council for Agricultural Science and Technology.

Scherer, C.W. 1990. National Risk Communication Workshop. Department of Communication. Ithaca, NY: Cornell University.

Webb, T., T. Lang, and K. Tucker. 1987. Food Irradiation, Who Wants It? Wellingborough, Great Britain: Thorsons Publishers.

Webb, T., and T. Lang. 1990. Food Irradiation: The Myth and the Reality. Wellingborough, Great Britain: Thorsons Publishers.

CHAPTER 5

THE ECONOMICS OF MARKETING IRRADIATED FOODS

DERMOT J. HAYES, PhD

Introduction

In a technical sense, the irradiation process improves the quality of irradiated foods either by reducing pathogenic contamination or by extending the maturation process. As with almost all improvements, there is an associated cost, and the question addressed in this chapter is how best to capture these increased costs in the marketing process. This issue is complicated because the benefits and costs of irradiation are small for the typical consumer. Meat that is already very safe will be made safer, fruit that already tastes good will taste better, and a marketing system that is probably the most efficient in the world will become slightly more efficient. In this climate, *perceptions* become as important as reality, and so long as a perception exists that the food might in any way be harmed by the process, there is little, by way of benefit, that the retailer can offer in return for the perceived damage that has been done.

The situation is further complicated by the desire of the United States media to be fair to both sides of every breaking story. Because society has decided that it needs to hear from both prosecution and defense, the U.S. economy has created a profitable niche for interest groups whose only apparent function is to slow the implementation of scientific advances. In this regard, the U.S. food system is held hostage to its own successes in that most consumers are justifiably pleased with the quality and value of foods and are loath to fix what is not broken.

111

Any new food process must survive serious attention by these professional devil's advocates, and only those products that offer clear and large advantages or that have strong advocacy groups are likely to survive.

To better understand the problems associated with marketing irradiated food, consider the advantages of a company marketing a fat substitute over one that must market an irradiated product. The company with the fat substitute can expect to capture all rights due to the owner of a successful patent and can therefore spend millions of dollars to get the product to market. It can also make claims about the health problems associated with eating too much fat because these claims cause trouble for someone else.

Because irradiation is a public good, no one firm or industry can expect to benefit from patent rights. This means that someone else must pay to get the product to market. Producers cannot be expected to do this because they would have to explain what is wrong with the current product, and for the poultry industry to advertise about *Salmonella* contamination or for the pork industry to mention *Trichinella* would be unprofitable. The scientific community may appreciate the benefits of the irradiation process, but individual scientists are paid to do research— not to participate in talk shows. If the scientists were to put themselves in a position to benefit, they would be criticized for having sold out to industry.

Large food companies have million-dollar brand names to protect and are not anxious to have these brands associated with a process as unprofitable and controversial as irradiation may be. Thus, at first glance, it would appear that food irradiation is an *orphan* process in that consumers do not have the time or inclination to learn of its benefits, and no one in the marketing system has the incentive to provide this information.

The situation just described is not unusual. The European Community (EC) recently banned the use of growth promotants in farm animals because of a similar alignment of forces. EC consumers now pay upward of 10% more for beef, yet no one seems to mind. Likewise, the introduction of microwave ovens was delayed for years by media stories about "escaping waves," and it was not until the process passed on to the Japanese that this U.S. technology was successfully marketed in the United States.

A story once heard at an irradiation conference makes the point most clearly:

> A new process called thermal radiation has been developed that improves both the texture and taste of some foods. This process also kills many known pathogens and extends the shelf life of some foods. Unfortunately, thermal radiation also reduces the vitamin content of some vegetables, produces detectable levels of benzene in eggs, and creates a charcoal-like carcinogen on the outside of meats. Therefore, this process, also known as cooking, has been banned pending further studies.

The preceding discussion makes clear the importance of getting the economics right when marketing irradiated foods. Surprisingly, there does seem to be one way to get this process to market. The next three sections of this chapter explain the economics behind this method, discuss how it would be implemented, and present the results of some ongoing work at Iowa State University that we believe shows that food irradiation can be marketed successfully and be profitable for the food industry.

Price-dependent Preferences

In a paper published in 1977, Pollack[8] argued that consumers sometimes allow their preferences or tastes to be influenced by prices. He called this phenomenon price-dependent preferences. This somewhat innocuous title describes one of the most successful and widely used marketing tools in use in the United States today.

Suppose you have developed a new type of wine, hair shampoo, or jeans. Suppose the wine is black, the shampoo blue, and the jeans have the zipper in the wrong place. It does not matter what the alteration is, so long as it is distinctive. Now suppose you want to introduce these products into a market that is already overcrowded and not in obvious need of improved products. Let's also assume that the product costs *less* to make than the existing competition. One possibility would be to attempt to undercut the market with a low introductory price, but imagine how wine critics would respond to a 99¢ bottle of black wine with a distinctive new flavor!

This is where Pollack's idea comes in. Pollack argued that our tastes depend on our perceptions of the cost of the product. For some products, such as wine or shampoo, we find it difficult to tell what is good and what is not good. It is not until we have been trained to identify the expensive product that we become experts.

There is nothing dishonest about this procedure. With sufficient exposure, we will actually reach the point where we prefer the taste we associate with the higher price. For example, in Ireland the working class drink Guiness beer and yuppies drink Budweiser or Heineken. In the United States, the yuppie drinks Guiness or Heineken, whereas in Holland, the working class drink Heineken. Likewise, one suspects that if caviar grew on peanut plants and peanut butter in the bellies of rare fish, gourmets would become ecstatic about the taste of various types of peanut butter while sending their kids to school with caviar sandwiches.

The trick to successfully introducing the distinctive new product is therefore to sell it at such a high price that almost no one can afford it. For products such as shampoo or jeans, for which this is impractical, one can also restrict the type of outlet that can sell the product. After several years, those with the more refined tastes will truly believe that black wine tastes better than red wine or that salon-purchased shampoos really are better. The rest of us will observe the willingness of these experts to part with large sums and we too will begin to make this association.

Now, all that is needed is for the marketing company to reduce the price of these new elitist products to where everybody can afford them. In our minds, the "normal" price for these products is the high price and we believe that we are getting a good deal because the "market" price is low. Thus, the product can be successfully launched on the mass market—even at prices that remain higher than those of the competition. This phenomenon also explains why it is so difficult to launch new cut-price products in markets where quality is a subjective issue.

Application of the Price-dependent Preferences Technique to Irradiated Foods

As mentioned, the principal problem with the irradiation process is that no one stands to benefit if the product is introduced. The solution is to market the process in such a way that each person who handles the irradiated product earns more than when they handle the nonirradiated product. The way to finance this difference is to charge large premiums for irradiated products. Rather than have the industry argue against having to label irradiated products, the label should be used as a badge of pride. At first, sales will be slow, as is currently the case for organic vegetables. But after a while, consumers will pause to decide whether they want the "*Salmonella*-free" chicken or the nonirradiated alternative–or fruit picked when ripe, versus fruit that "ripens" on the way to the store. Not everybody will pay an extra 20¢ or 30¢ per pound for irradiated chicken, but at this kind of premium, only a small sales volume would be needed to make it viable. Those who would pay the premium will include opinion leaders and many consumers who will try it once to see if there is any difference. As long as consumers have a clear choice, consumer pressure groups will have little to complain about because most of their current arguments will become redundant.

This solution precludes the big brand names, and that may be just as well. These firms have too much to lose and are too easily a target for the kind of propaganda that has been developed against irradiated foods.

The kind of company that will find a market niche is the smaller company that is trying to create profitable new brands and is prepared to take the risks that are involved. These small companies create a much less attractive target and may be able to offer a more effective counter-argument than either scientists or the representatives of large multinational corporations.

Iowa State University Research on Marketing Irradiated Meats

To test the preceding hypothesis (i.e., that some consumers would, under the right conditions, pay a substantial premium for irradiated foods), the author and four colleagues at Iowa State University designed a series of experiments to replicate the actual point-of-purchase decision of consumers encountering irradiated meats the first time.[1] These experiments are very different from survey results because we required the individuals to pay their own money to eat irradiated meats (or to avoid eating irradiated meats). Because Iowa State University possesses a custom-built meat irradiator, we could serve irradiated meat and show participants how the irradiator works.

We conducted experiments with both irradiated pork and irradiated chicken. Because our experimental procedure was similar in both cases, it is worth summarizing here. First, groups of approximately 15 participants were brought to the Iowa State University Meat Lab, where we explained the experimental procedure. The mechanism we used is called a second-price Vickrey sealed bid auction, which involved 20 rounds of bidding.[15] In each case, we made known only what the second-highest price in the previous bid had been. At the end of 20 bidding rounds, we randomly selected one bidding round as the binding round, and the person with the highest bid in that round got to purchase a meal at the second-highest price bid in that round. This procedure—although somewhat complicated—has the advantage of forcing participants to write down their true or honest bid in each round.[15] Thus, it is best to think of the experiment as an auction where everybody has the incentive to bid honestly without regard for what others are doing. Because of this complexity, we held several practice runs with candy bars before introducing the irradiated meat.

In some experiments, each participant owned an irradiated meal and was asked to bid to get an otherwise identical nonirradiated meal. In other experiments, the participants owned a typical meal and were asked to bid to upgrade to an irradiated meal.

If the participants bid to purchase an irradiated meal, it showed either that they were anxious to try this new product or that they did not want to take a chance that the typical chicken meal was contaminated with *Salmonella* (or the pork with *Trichinella*). We were able to vouch for the safety of the irradiated food, but we were unable to guarantee the safety of the typical meal.

After 10 bidding trials, the participants were given a tour of the irradiation facility. We were then able to measure how the bids reacted once the participants had seen the machine and realized that we had in fact irradiated the food.

For the pork experiments, we did not attempt to subdivide the subjects based on their perceptions about the process. In the chicken experiments, however, we allocated participants based on their answers to a phone survey conducted prior to the experiment. In the pork experiments, we first used Iowa State University students and then expanded to the general population by getting consumers at a local supermarket to sign up. In the poultry experiments, we used a scientifically selected random sample from the local area (Story County, Iowa).

Figures 5.1 and 5.2 show the results for the student-based pork experiments. None of the students wanted to bid to upgrade from an irradiated meal to a typical one, and the average bid lines in Figure 5.2 run along the bottom of the chart. In the experiments where we asked the participants to bid to upgrade to an irradiated meal, the average bids ranged from approximately 45¢ in Experiment 1 to approximately $1 in Experiment 3 (see Figures 5.1 and 5.3).

Because the Iowa State University meat irradiator had just started operations, these students had been exposed to irradiation stories both in the student-run newspaper and the local daily newspaper. Given the nature of this exposure, it came as a surprise that all 60 of the participants favored the irradiated product. We were also surprised at how

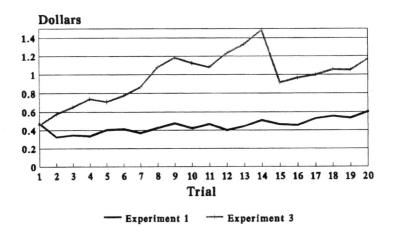

FIGURE 5.1. Willingness of undergraduate subjects to pay to upgrade from a nonirradiated meal to an irradiated meal.

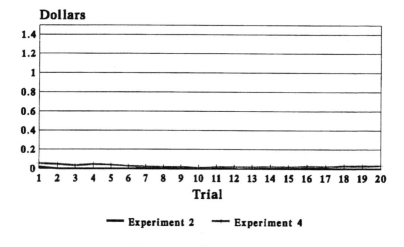

FIGURE 5.2. Willingness of undergraduate subjects to pay to up-grade from an irradiated meal to a nonirradiated meal.

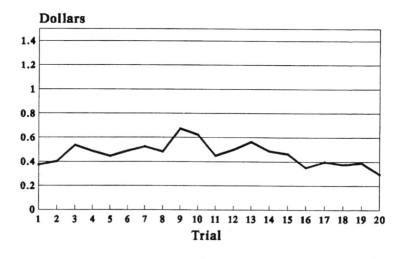

FIGURE 5.3. Willingness of adult subjects to pay to upgrade from a nonirradiated meal to an irradiated meal.

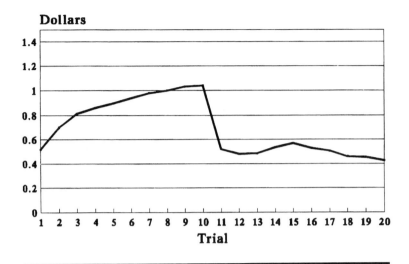

FIGURE 5.4. Willingness of adult subjects to pay to upgrade from an irradiated meal to a nonirradiated meal.

much of their own money they were prepared to pay to taste an irradiated sandwich.

When we extended the pork experiment to adults taken at random from a local food store, we found that about one-half of the 30 participants given the irradiated sandwich were prepared to pay to upgrade to a nonirradiated sandwich. Likewise, about one-half of those given a typical sandwich were prepared to pay to upgrade to an irradiated sandwich. The average bids from both experiments are shown in Figures 5.3 and 5.4. Notice how the size of the bid to avoid the irradiated sandwich fell after we showed them the machine and explained how it worked. This result makes the obvious point that the less people know about the process, the more they fear it. Notice also that the size of the bid to purchase the irradiated meal among the food-store-based participants was lower than among the students, settling at approximately 30¢.

We were intrigued by these results and so decided both to do a better job of sample selection and to compare people's perceptions with the way they performed in the experiments. Therefore, in a second set of experiments—with irradiated chicken—we purchased the phone numbers of a representative sample of Story County residents and conducted a phone survey before asking them to participate in the experiment. Story County, Iowa, contains a reasonable balance between urban and rural residents and also has a reasonable cross section of the various professional classes. It represents middle America in the same way as Peoria, Illinois.

Of the 183 people we surveyed, approximately 73% said they would prefer irradiated meat, 9% said they had no preference. This left 41 respondents who, after a scientific explanation of the irradiation process, said that they would prefer nonirradiated meat.

We then invited representatives from both groups to participate in the experiments. Of the 58 participants who said they preferred the irradiated meat, the average willingness to pay, as given in the hypothetical phone survey, was 58¢. When we ran these people through the nonhypothetical experiment, this bid fell to 44¢. We had expected bids to be higher in this group than for the adults in the pork experiment because we had preselected from among the 71% who favored the irradiated products. We also expected bids to fall once the participants had to pay money out of pocket to upgrade to the irradiated meal. The only surprising thing is that the bids did not fall by more.

This pro-irradiation sample represented approximately 70% of the total we called, and these participants were willing to pay an average of 44¢ to taste irradiated meat. Of course, many of these were bidding to taste a "new" product and may not have cared that it was safer. Nevertheless, these individuals obviously represent a large and potentially profitable niche market.

Among the subset who expressed a dislike for irradiated foods, the average hypothetical bid to avoid the irradiated meat was $1.85. However, when we put these same people in an experimental setting where they actually had to pay the amount they quoted, this bid fell to only 39¢. This result means that, among those surveyed, participants who opposed irradiation were much more likely to exaggerate than those who said they liked the process. This is an intriguing result in that it points to a potential bias in survey results as compared to how people would actually behave at the point of purchase.

From the perspective of those who may be in the business of selling irradiated foods, the evidence may be summarized as follows. A majority of the participants in our representative survey were in favor of eating irradiated foods, and many of them were prepared to pay approximately 30¢ per pound for this opportunity. More research needs to be done before these results can be translated to a national level, but the evidence to date is supportive of the hypothesis mentioned earlier; namely, that there are enough people who would pay enough money to constitute a profitable niche market.

Costs and Benefits of Food Irradiation

The previous section examined how irradiated foods could best be marketed. Implicit in this argument was that the process itself would be worthwhile, i.e., that its benefits would exceed its costs. This section examines (a) how different levels of irradiation influence the safety of the food; (b) the cost of irradiating food to achieve different levels of pathogen reduction; and (c) the willingness of consumers to pay for an increase in food safety. This section focuses on *Salmonella* contamination of poultry because it is the only pathogen for which full cost benefit analysis is available. It is fortunate and coincidental that two separate studies have examined this issue. The first study by Dick Perrin examines the cost of irradiating poultry at different dose levels and the influence of dose levels on *Salmonella*.[7] The second study by the author and others at Iowa State University examines consumers' willingness to pay for changes in the probability of *Salmonella*.[2] Both of these papers are somewhat technical and too complicated for purposes of this chapter. Hence, the discussion presented below captures only those results necessary to conduct the cost-benefit analysis. The reader is referred to the original work for further details.

Before presenting this analysis, it is worth discussing terminology. Food scientists measure food safety by measuring the number of microorganisms per square centimeter of tissue surface. This number is typically reported in terms of the base 10 logarithm. An increase in food safety occurs when the number of pathogens falls by one log. A one log reduction means that 90% of the original contaminants have been killed; a 2 log reduction (or 2 dLogU) implies a 99% reduction; etc.

Irradiation dosage is measured in kiloGrays (kGys), which measure the amount of energy absorbed per kilogram of meat. The number of kGys required to reduce the pathogenic contamination by 1 log is called the D_{10} value. The threshold level, at which flavor changes occur, is about 2.5 kGys.

Table 5.1 reports some dosage response work for various pathogens. Table 5.2 is a meta analysis of Table 5.1 and shows the dosage response rate. The safety factor S is closely related to the num-

Table 5.1. Summary of results from meat irradiation experiments

Authors and Reference No.	Dose (kGy)	Log U cntl	Log U tmt	dLogU	Meat	Pathogen
Thayer et al.[13]	1.1	9.0	7.4	−1.6	Chicken	*Salmonella*
Thayer and Boyd[11]	1.6	9.2	5.8	−3.4	Chicken	*Salmonella*
Thayer and Boyd[12]	2.7	9.6	3.2	−6.4	Chicken	*Salmonella*
Varabioff et al.[14]	2.5	8.6	0.0	−8.6	Chicken	*Listeria*
Huhtanen[3]	1.2	8.6	5.7	−2.9	Chicken	*Listeria*
Lamulka et al.[4]	2.5	5.8	2.7	−3.1	Chicken	*Yersinia*
Lamulka et al.[4]	2.5	4.6	0.6	−3.9	Chicken	*Campylobacter*
Perrin[7]	1.3	2.3	1.0	−1.2	Pork	*Clostridium*
Lebepe et al.[5]	3.0	2.6	1.2	−1.5	Pork	aerobics
Perrin[7]	1.8	4.0	2.0	−2.0	Chicken	aerobics
Tarkowski[10]	1.0	5.6	2.4	−3.2	Beef	*Enterobacter*
Tarkowski[10]	1.0	—	—	−7.9	Beef	various
AVE – all	1.8	—	—	−3.6		
those w/dLogU	1.9	6.0	2.7	−3.2		

Note: cntl = control; tmt = treated; AVE = average.

Table 5.2. The safety function evaluated for pathogenic microorganisms under commercial conditions

Irradiation Dose (kGy)	Reduction in Microorganisms (dLogU)	Safety (S)
0.0	0.0	−1.000
0.5	−0.34	−0.452
1.0	−0.60	−0.252
1.5	−0.83	−0.148
2.0	−1.04	−0.090
2.5	−1.25	−0.056
3.0	−1.44	−0.036
5.0	−2.17	−0.007

Source: From Perrin.[7]

ber of pathogens on the meat (S =−1/exp [2.3 dLogU]). It arbitrarily defines the original contamination level as equal to −1 and, as this number approaches zero, the safety level improves. For example, a safety level of −0.1 means that 90% of the bacteria have been killed. From Table 5.2, we can see that a dose of 1 kGy increases safety by 75%, while a dose of 2.5 kGys increases safety by 94%.

Table 5.3 shows some irradiation cost estimates taken from Roberts.[9] As expected, the cost decreases with the size of the facility and increases with the dose. Perrin fitted a translog cost function to this data and found that a 100% increase in the dose (i.e., from 1 kGy to 2 kGys) increases costs by approximately 10%, holding all else constant.

The last piece of information required is how much consumers are willing to pay to reduce the *Salmonella* content of poultry, i.e., to have the benefits of irradiation. In a series of experiments similar to those described in the early part of this chapter, we asked students to bid to upgrade from unsafe poultry. Students were given a *Salmonella*-contaminated sandwich and told that they would not receive their $20 participation fee unless they ate the sandwich. We did, however, offer them the opportunity of upgrading to a safe sandwich. We ran the experiment seven times, changing the contamination level tenfold with

Table 5.3. Summary of budgeted irradiation costs

Volume (million pounds per year)	Dosage (kGy)	Annual Cost (million $)	Labor Share of Costs	Capital Share of Costs	"Other" Share of Costs	Cost per Pound (cents)
52	2.50	0.77	0.303	0.402	0.295	1.487
104	2.50	0.94	0.311	0.397	0.292	0.905
208	2.50	1.28	0.274	0.418	0.308	0.616
416	2.50	2.16	0.217	0.451	0.333	0.520
104	1.25	0.83	0.352	0.374	0.274	0.800
208	1.25	1.00	0.350	0.375	0.275	0.482
416	1.25	1.40	0.334	0.384	0.282	0.337
520	0.25	1.14	0.411	0.340	0.250	0.219
26	5.00	0.66	0.226	0.447	0.327	2.551
52	5.00	0.79	0.248	0.434	0.318	1.512
104	5.00	1.08	0.216	0.452	0.332	1.041
208	5.00	1.93	0.151	0.488	0.360	0.930
26	10.00	0.78	0.257	0.428	0.314	2.989
52	10.00	1.02	0.212	0.454	0.334	1.953
104	10.00	1.81	0.129	0.501	0.370	1.743

Source: Adapted from Roberts.[9]

each experiment. We then regressed the average bid on the safety level. The results show that participants would pay 30¢ more for each one log reduction in the probability of becoming sick.[2]

Putting all of these numbers together, we find that a one log increase in safety can be achieved with about 2 kGys. This treatment would cost between 0.5¢ and 2¢, depending on the size of the irradiation facility. This tenfold increase in safety would be worth 30¢ per meal to consumers; thus, the technology has a return ratio between 15:1 and 60:1. These results point to an unambiguous conclusion. When the question is phrased correctly, i.e., in terms of the benefits of safer food, most Americans would be more than willing to pay for food irradiation.

Conclusions

It does not seem likely that irradiated foods will be mass marketed under existing brand names. However, there does seem to be a relatively large subgroup who would be prepared to pay for safer, irradiated foods. This chapter has argued that by selling irradiated foods at a substantial margin—10¢ to 30¢ extra per pound—a profitable niche market for irradiated foods could survive. The anti-irradiation lobby would find it difficult to argue against this type of marketing campaign because it would be conducted by small firms that would sell irradiated foods as a premium product. Should irradiated foods be introduced in this way, many would come to view this process as *desirable*, and once this perception occurs, consumers will be prepared to take the time to learn about the process. Should industry try to sell irradiated foods as *acceptable*, the peculiar dynamics of the U.S. marketplace will make it difficult to introduce the process.

Results reported in this paper show that once the acceptability problem is resolved, the process will be widely used. This is true because the increase in food safety resulting from irradiation is worth between 15 and 60 times the cost of the process itself.

References

1. Fox, John A., Dermot J. Hayes, Jason F. Shogren, and James B. Kliebenstein. 1994. Effects of alternative descriptions of food irradiation on

preferences for irradiated pork in experimental auctions. In Essays in the Measurement of Consumer Preferences in Experimental Auction Markets. PhD diss. Iowa State University, Ames.

2. Hayes, Dermot J., Jason F. Shogren, Seung Youll Shin, and James B. Kliebenstein. 1995. Valuing good safety in experimental auction markets. *Am. J. Agric. Econ.* In press.

3. Huhtanen, C.N., R.K. Jenkins, and D.W. Thayer. 1989. Gamma Radiation Sensitivity of *Listeria monocytogenes. J. Food Prot.* 52:610-13.

4. Lamulka, P.O., G.R. Sunki, D.R. Chawan, D.R. Rao, and L.A. Shackelford. 1992. Bacteriological quality of freshly processed broiler chickens as affected by carcass pretreatment and gamma irradiation. *J. Food Sci.* 57:330-32.

5. Lebepe, S., R.A. Molins, S.P Charoen., H. Farrar IV., and R.P. Skowronski. 1990. Changes in microflora and other characteristics of vacuum-packaged pork loins irradiated at 3.0 kGy. *J. Food Sci.* 55:918-24.

6. Morrison, Rosanna M. 1989. An economic analysis of electron accelerators and cobalt-60 for irradiating food. Technical Bull. No. 1762, CED/ERS U.S. Department of Agriculture, Washington, DC.

7. Perrin, Richard K. 1992. Technology assessment related to food-borne disease control. Unpublished manuscript (April), Iowa State University, Ames, IA.

8. Pollack, Robert A. 1977. Price dependent preferences. *Am. Econ. Rev.* (67):64-75.

9. Roberts, Tanya. 1989. Human illness costs of foodborne bacteria. *Am. J. Agric. Econ.* 71(2):468-74.

10. Tarkowski, J.A., S.C.C. Stoffer, R.R. Beumer, and E.H. Kampelmacher. 1984a. Low dose gamma irradiation of raw meat. I. Bacteriological and sensory quality effects in artificially contaminated samples. *Int. J. Food Microbiol.* 1:13-23.

11. Thayer, D.W., and G. Boyd. 1991a. Effect of ionizing radiation dose, temperature, and atmosphere on the survival of *Salmonella typhimurium* in sterile, mechanically deboned chicken meat. *Poultry Sci.* 70:381-88.

12. Thayer, D.W., and G. Boyd. 1991b. Survival of *Salmonella typhimurium* ATCC 14028 on the surface of chicken legs or in mechanically deboned chicken meat, gamma irradiated in air or vacuum at temperatures of −20 to +20 degrees C. *Poultry Sci.* 70:1,026-33.

13. Thayer, D.W., S. Songprasertchai, and G. Boyd. 1991. Effects of heat and ionizing radiation on *Salmonella typhimurium* in mechanically deboned chicken meat. *J. Food Prot.* 54:718-24.

14. Varabioff, Y., G.E. Mitchell, and S.M. Nottingham. 1992. Effects of irradiation on bacterial load and *Listeria monocytogenes* in raw chicken. *J. Food Prot.* 55:389-91.

15. Vickery, W. 1961. Counterspeculation, auctions and competitive sealed tenders. *J. of Financ.* (16):8-37.

Selected Readings

American Meat Institute. 1988 (and earlier editions). *Meat Facts*. Washington, DC.

Anderson, M.E., H.E. Huff, H.D. Naumann, R.T. Marshall, J.M. Damare, M. Pratt, and R. Johnston. 1987. Evaluation of an automated beef carcass washing and sanitizing system under production conditions. *J. Food Prot.* 50:562-66.

Maddala, G.S., and R.B. Roberts. 1980. Alternative Functional Forms and Errors of Pseudo Data Estimation. *Rev. Econ. Stat.* 62:323-27.

Urbain, Walter M. 1986. *Food Irradiat*. Academic Press, Orlando, FL.

INDEX

127

130